Joe Taylor's

Complete Guide to Breeding and Raising Racehorses

*Advice From
America's Master Horseman*

Joseph Lannon Taylor

Library of Congress Cataloging-in-Publication Data

Taylor, Joseph Lannon, 1924-
　　Joe Taylor's complete guide to breeding and raising racehorses : advice from America's master horseman / Joseph Lannon Taylor.
　　Includes bibliographical references and index.
　　ISBN 0-929346-20-3 : $40.00
　　1. Race horses. 2. Race horses--Breeding. 3. Horse farms.
　I. Title. II. Title : Complete guide to breeding and raising racehorses.
SF338. T38　1992
636. 1 ' 2--dc20　　　　　　　　　　　　　　　　92-39991
　　　　　　　　　　　　　　　　　　　　　　　　CIP

Published by:

The Russell Meerdink Company, Ltd.
1555 South Park Avenue
Neenah, WI　54956
(414) 725-0955 Worldwide

Printed in the United States of America

This book is dedicated to my mother,
Mary Catherine Lannon Taylor,
to my mentor and friend John Gaines
and to my wife who made it all worthwhile,
Mary Emily Marshall Taylor.

Acknowledgments

There are many people who contributed to this book, either directly or indirectly. I want to thank all those who taught me, encouraged me and believed in me. My success is a reflection of the quality of business associates and friends that have made up my life in the racing industry.

For their technical assistance with this book and for their expertise and dedication which makes my job easier, I want to thank Dr. Scott W. Pierce of Rood & Riddle Equine Hospital and Mr. Kenneth Cromwell of Mid-America Nutritional Consultants. For all this and for being my sons, too, I thank Duncan, Frank, Ben and Mark Taylor.

For giving me my start in the racehorse business, I thank Mr. Gene Sears and Mr. Clarence Gaines. For taking me to the top and for creating the best professional relationship a man ever had, I thank Mr. John Gaines.

For making my years at Gainesway and at Taylor Made such a pleasure, I thank the employees, business associates and friends, including Satish Seemar, whose likeness and skill in the round pen appears in the Yearling Management chapter.

For the generous use of their photographs to illustrate my ideas, I thank Suzie Oldham, Martin Pierce, Photos by Z, Lee P. Thomas, Joy Gilbert, Gainesway Farm, the *Thoroughbred Times*, *Hoof Beats Magazine*, Judy Hanson and Dr. O. J. Ginther of the University of Wisconsin Veterinary School.

For their hard work, encouragement and enthusiasm for what this book could be, I thank my publishers, Russell and Jan Meerdink, and for editing my work, Sara Heironimus.

Contents

Part I - Building the Horse Farm

Location   Size   Price and Improvements   Grass   Rolling Land   Water   Trees   Growing Crops   Buying an Existing Horse Farm   Converting Other Types of Farms

Segmenting the Farm   Location of Barns   Roads   Paddocks   Pastures   Waterers   Run-in Sheds   Houses   Outbuildings   Manure Pits   Co-mingling Horses and Other Livestock

Height   Posts   Boards   Batten strips   Construction   Painting   Diamond Mesh Fences   Electric and Barbed Wire Fences   Plastic Fencing   Gate Entrances   Pipe Gates, Width and Swing   Slam Posts   Gate Posts   Automatic Gates   Double Swinging Gates   Gate Latches   Hinges

Establishing Pastures   Pasture Maintenance   Harrowing   Manure Spreading   Protecting the Trees

Site Selection, Grade and Drainage   Floors   Construction Materials   Insulation   Ventilation   Shape   Height   Aisles and Stall Placement   Stall Design   Stall Size   Foaling Stalls   Walls   Crossties   Stall Hardware and Latches   Washracks   Right-Angle Turns   Roofs   Windows   Storage   Lights and Wiring   Fire Protection   Resources for Fighting Fires   Planning for Emergencies   Water   Feed Tubs   Exercise Pavilions   Walkways

Part II - Finding and Breeding Good Horses

Part III - Horse Farm Management

Feeding the Foal   Handling the Foal's Feet   Monitoring the Legs   Periosteal Stripping Mudding the Foal's Legs Weaning Proper Weanling Care

The author, Joseph Lannon Taylor.
(Photo courtesy of Lee P. Thomas)

Foreword

It was in the fall of 1952 that Joe Taylor accompanied by his wife, Mary Emily, answered a help wanted ad that my father, C. F. Gaines, master of Gainesway Farm, placed in the classified pages of the Lexington, Kentucky Herald Leader.

I listened to my father interview Joe and then watched as he examined the palms of Joe's hands to see if they had any calluses. A deal was made but certainly none of us realized at the time that the destinies of Gainesway Farm and Joe Taylor would be one and the same.

It took all of one year for Joe to advance from stall mucker and yearling groom to Farm Manager and star salesman. Under Joe's guidance, Gainesway was to own or breed without exception the winners of every major trotting horse stakes in North America, including the Hambletonian twice and the Kentucky Futurity four times.

When I established Gainesway Farm's Thoroughbred division in November, 1962, we grew from one stallion and a handfull of mares into an operation of forty stallions breeding two thousand mares a year. Five Gainesway stallions were to lead the Sires List in America, England and France and their progeny included two winners of the Kentucky Derby and eight winners of the Prix de l'Arc de Triomphe.

In the breeding shed, on the race track and in the sales ring, Gainesway Farm's record speaks for itself and is irrefutable evidence of the high professionalism and keen intelligence that Joe Taylor brings to every aspect of Thoroughbred Breeding and Racing.

At the highest level, a Farm Manager must play many roles. Joe is not only a complete horseman but he is also an agronomist, builder, geneticist, caretaker, nutritionist, salesman, entrepreneur, executive, promoter, accountant, arborist, midwife, dealmaker, diplomat and handyman. Joe is truly a man for all seasons but everyone who knows him understands that his real business is helping people and that is why he wrote this book.

This Complete Guide to Breeding and Raising Racehorses will surely become a classic of its type and could only have been written by someone with the lived experience and communication skills of my comrade-at-arms these many years, Joe Taylor.

I must extend one word of caution to you readers, Joe would be the first to tell you that if you don't get calluses on your hands after reading this book, it won't do you that much good.

John R. Gaines
Lexington, Kentucky
June 11, 1993

Introduction

I can't remember a time when I was not in love with Kentucky and the dream of raising good horses.

It really all began with my great, great, grandfather Reuben Taylor. Back in the 1760s he travelled from Virginia to what is now Winchester, KY. He came to Kentucky as a surveyor. Eventually, he settled in Clark County, Kentucky, where he built a small house with only two rooms and a small hallway. He went back to Virginia and told others what he did. When he returned to Kentucky with his wife and two brothers, (including Hub Taylor, one of the founding fathers of Newport, Kentucky) they discovered that the house had been destroyed by Indians. He rebuilt it and to this day, it stands, near the family cemetery, as the oldest house in Clark County, Kentucky. Since that time, my family have been Kentuckians.

My mother was a Lannon. Her great-great grandparents came from Ireland while they were young. They came to Kentucky to farm. So you can say that I've got generations of "bluegrass" in my blood.

Things weren't easy, but there was an economic boom in 1919 and 1920 when tobacco prices were high and my father made some money. He and his father had a transfer wagon partnership doing road work and hauling rock to Keeneland to build walls.

I was born in 1924 at St. Joseph Hospital in Lexington, KY. Around 1927, times got tough and we moved to Franklin County to begin farming. My parents were always in fear of losing the farm, but my three brothers and four sisters and I went to school and were very happy. We didn't have much, but we never thought we were poor either. In fact, we were better off than most people at that time.

My first experience with breeding horses occurred when I was eight or 10 years old. All his life my father worked with Trotting horses. My mother wasn't too happy about his interest because she was afraid he'd lose what little money we had. My father decided to have his favorite mare bred to Sam Luck's stallion, Spencer. The stud fee was $100. Because he didn't want my mother to know about it, he sent me to Mr. Luck's with the mare, saying, "Don't you say a word to your mother." Mr. Luck bred the mare, but wouldn't let me observe the breeding. Later, my father asked me, "Are you sure you bred her to the right horse?" "Well," I said, "I don't know. He wouldn't let me in the breeding shed to watch." My father was really upset, but things worked out well in the end because he sold that weanling for $600, which probably saved the farm.

I attended a two-room school in Alton, Kentucky until the sixth grade. I didn't like school and wasn't much of a student. I quit while I was in high school. Little did I know that my education was just beginning. I share-cropped and worked with horses. I knew how to break horses, drive horses and ride horses. American Saddle Horses were my first love, but I also had a few Standardbreds.

After I had been working a few years for myself, I enlisted in the Army. After my discharge, Mary Emily Marshall and I began dating and we were married in 1946.

It's difficult to put into words what Mary Emily has contributed to my life. Her strong character and values, her faith and her patience have strengthened and sustained us all. When work took me away, she supported our children and she never complained. Eventually, we were blessed with six boys and two girls and with that many children, there's always something going on. But Mary Emily always knew what was happening and, in her quiet way, she taught all eight of them right from wrong. Marrying Mary Emily will always be my best decision.

Looking back, I realize neither Mary Emily nor I knew of the hard times that awaited us. She had a good job as Assistant City Clerk in Frankfort, I was working and the future seemed bright. But it was tough making money with horses - I didn't know how to sell and I didn't know bloodlines. After a few bad years of farming, I found myself with a wife, two small children and more debts than I could handle. Just when it looked like we weren't going to make it, Gene Sears offered me a job as a groom at Roosevelt Raceway in Long Island, New York. Mary Emily realized it was a chance to gain the knowledge I needed to make a living with horses. With her encouragement, I made arrangements with the bank and the people to whom I owed money and struck off for New York. I learned a great deal at Roosevelt, working my way up to second trainer for Mr. Sears and meeting a lot of fine people in the process. It was a good move.

After a year I returned to Kentucky. I answered an ad for an assistant farm manager's job. A couple of days later I received a call from my father's friend Leslie Morris in Frankfort. He told me that Clarence Gaines from Gainesway Farm had called him regarding my application. He said, "I told him you could do anything he had. He'll be calling you in a few days."

That was in November, 1951 and by that summer, Mr. Gaines made me the Farm Manager. I worked for the Gaines family until John Gaines, Clarence's son, sold the farm in 1990. I've learned and done a lot of things with John Gaines in the horse business. Prior to 1963, we bred only Standardbreds. Then in 1963 John bought his first Thoroughbred. That was to be the beginning of one of the greatest Thoroughbred farms in the history of racing.

We began our stallion operation with Fred Hooper's stallion, Crozier and when I retired in 1990, Gainesway stood as many as 42 stallions, among them top horses such as Lyphard, Riverman, Blushing Groom, Vaguely Noble, Bold Bidder and Sharpen Up. Along the way, John Gaines and I introduced many concepts to the breeding business. John Gaines was a great man to work for, a genius really. Through his vision we perfected the Mare's Lights Program, improved stallion management to decrease covers and developed many horse farms along the way. It was our goal to give the mare owner who brought his mare to Gainesway Farm the best service and the best chance of getting his mare in foal. Thanks to John Gaines, I had the freedom and the resources to realize this goal.

After retiring from Gainesway, I joined my sons, Duncan, Frank, Ben and Mark at Taylor Made Farm. While I intended to serve as an advisor, I remain involved in all aspects of the farm business, from seasons and shares to foaling to the latest nutritional and veterinary information. It is a fascinating, absorbing life and has given me a richly rewarding career. I hope to share some of the rewards with you in this book.

Disclaimer

The purpose of this book is to acquaint the reader with the methods and procedures used by the author in breeding and raising racehorses. The information is drawn from the author's extensive experience working with horses and managing breeding farms.

It is not all-inclusive, however, and is not intended to cover all circumstances or every situation which may arise. Neither the author nor the publisher make any representations or warranties, either express or implied, regarding the techniques discussed and assume no liability therefore.

Part I

Building the Horse Farm

Chapter 1

Finding the Right Land

There comes a time when a man dreams of giving up the pressures of his business, the congestion of the city and the fast pace at which he is living. If he has ever been around a horse, has been to the races or if his wife has wanted to own a horse ever since she was a little girl, the dream soon becomes a desire to own a horse farm.

The day you decide to get into the horse business, you are really getting yourself into two businesses. You are in the horse business by design and in the real estate business by default. You can make or lose a lot of money in either business. Let me begin by telling you what I have learned about the real estate part of the horse business.

Location: The location of a horse farm is important. One bonus of owning a horse farm is that you can profitably control a large tract of land while waiting for development to reach you. Buy and develop your horse farm on the side of town where development is heading in your direction. Someday, you will want to sell the farm. It is a lot easier to sell at a profit if the land can be used for something other than raising horses. Don't get stuck with a piece of land which is unlikely to appreciate over time. In the real estate business, location is everything. This is particularly true for horse farms.

Your farm's location in proximity to other horse farms will affect its operating efficiency and value. Veterinarians and farriers are more accessible in those areas where most of their clients are located. If an emergency arises, you should have access to a vet or a farrier no more than 20 minutes away. Veterinary specialists, too, are readily available in areas that raise horses. If you have an orthopedic problem, for instance, you'll find that the most qualified experts are located in areas where valuable horses are raised. If your farm is the only horse farm within 100 miles, it might be difficult to find a veterinarian who specializes.

Labor also is a consideration. Racehorses need knowledgeable people to care for them and such people can be hard to find. Areas near racetracks and other breeding farms usually have a trained labor pool. It is easier to hire a qualified farm manager in Kentucky or Florida than in Wisconsin. Experienced mare managers are difficult to find outside of major horse breeding areas. If you locate in an area away from other farms, you may need to hire your key people from outside your area and train all other employees.

Size: There is an old rule of thumb that says a horse farm needs about five acres of pasture for every horse. I don't know how this got started. In Kentucky, there isn't a horse alive that can eat all the grass that grows on 2 1/2 acres. Depending upon the layout, I think that 2 1/2 acres of pasture per horse is about right. This may vary in other parts of the country. Of course, you will need additional land for roads, barns and other buildings. This brings the total to about four acres per horse. Four barns of 20 stalls each will need around 320 acres of land.

Price and Improvements: Pay attention to the price you pay for the land. If you plan to pay $10,000 an acre, you had better have some mighty good horses to put on it and some good luck to go with them. Good horse land is not necessarily expensive land. A well-known breeder proved that. He bought land right next to a top Thoroughbred farm for a few hundred dollars an acre and built good, but not expensive, barns on it. He bred two Kentucky Derby winners on that land. Horses bred on cheap land will run just as fast as horses bred on expensive land.

A horse farm should never be over-improved. Always keep in mind how, someday, you will get your money out of it. If you over-improve the property, the land value will never catch up with the cost of the improvements. Since there is no way to increase the value of the over-improved farm, you find yourself with a property that is difficult to sell at a profit.

Growing Grass: Good grass is *the* key ingredient to raising good horses. If you can't grow good grass, you can't grow good horses. The land must support a good growth of grass year after year. It need not be the best crop land but it must be strong land that can grow good grass.

A fellow once told me that the quickest way to evaluate farmland in Kentucky is to stand on the highest point of the land and count all the tobacco barns. If you see quite a few, you are standing on good land. If you can't see any at all, the land probably isn't much good. This may not always hold true, but good farmland capable of growing grass usually has a history of farming.

You need land that will support grass with only periodic fertilization. Silt and loam-type soils, soils that are not overly sandy or predominantly clay with a neutral to slightly acid pH are best. Well-balanced soil will sustain the grass year after year with only periodic additions of phosphate, nitrogen and potash.

The land around Lexington has a layer of limestone under it which is thought to add important minerals to the grass and the water. On some of the land, the limestone is at or near the surface with the average soil depth being about eight inches. I don't mind land that has a little rock on it. If I planned to plow or cultivate the land, I would want to be where the soil was a little deeper. But you don't need that kind of land to raise horses.

If you are not familiar with farming and soil types, seek the advice of someone who is. You need to know what grasses can be grown and maintained in your particular area. A good source for such information is your county agent or the school of agriculture at your state university.

Rolling Land: I like a horse farm to be a rolling farm. It should have some up and down grades to it for several reasons. Rolling land offers better drainage than land that is flat. Good drainage is worth a lot in the horse business. If the land does not drain properly, pastures and paddocks will be muddy for a long time after a rain. The action of the horses' hooves cuts into the ground, destroying the grass wherever there is standing water. No matter how capable the land may be of growing good grass, the pasture will be destroyed by horses standing and running on muddy fields. Even a moderate rainfall on poorly drained land is a problem. Every low spot becomes a dangerous quagmire for horses, causing falls, pulled shoes and strained muscles. In winter, low spots become skating rinks.

I also believe horses develop better on land that is rolling. Most horses exercise themselves and I believe they tend to build themselves up by running up and down the hills. You don't need a mountain for proper exercise, but get some land that has a roll to it.

Horses benefit from rolling land. *(Photo courtesy of Suzie Oldham)*

Water: A horse farm uses a lot of water and you will need a good, reliable source. Each paddock and pasture needs its own source of water. If you are able to tap into a municipal water system, do it. In the long run, it will be your most reliable and least expensive source. If city water is not available, you will need to drill one or several deep wells.

Sometimes it is possible to use creeks or springs as a water source. A spring-fed creek is an ideal source of fresh water. The trees that grow around the area provide shade and relief from the summer heat. An overflow pipe with a float valve is all that is needed to keep a water trough filled with fresh, clear spring water. But if you plan to use a creek, be certain you are dealing with fresh, flowing water. The source of the water must be fenced off so horses cannot enter the creek. If the creek is used as a wading pool by horses - or any livestock - it is ruined as a source of drinking water.

I don't like man-made ponds as a source of water for horses. They look nice but become stagnant quickly. If the water does not flow freely, you will have a lot of sick horses. The only way to use a man-made pond as a source of water is to keep the stock from standing in it and to install an overflow pipe. Even with these precautions, it may fail to provide fresh water. Consider your pond landscaping - stock it with fish or fowl - but keep your horses away from it.

Trees: Trees are an asset to the horse farm. They provide shade for horses and add character to the land. Suitable trees for the horse farm are non-poisonous and low maintenance. Avoid varieties of trees that shed fruit, berries, blossoms or small branches after every storm that must be cleaned up before turning out horses. Trees and shrubs that are toxic to horses include ornamental yews, black walnut, cherry and red maple trees. Consult your agricultural agent for varieties in your area which may be harmful to horses.

Do not confuse trees with a forest. Trees must be fenced out of a paddock and enclosed within a pasture. Heavily wooded land is not suitable for a horse farm. The expense of cutting many acres of trees and clearing the area of stumps and roots can be prohibitive.

Growing Crops: You may be tempted to raise your own oats and hay. There are two problems with this idea: (1) If your farm is located near major horsebreeding centers, such as Lexington or Ocala, you do not have the right climate for raising these crops. It's almost impossible to properly cure (dry) hay in the humid weather of the southeastern United States. You will have a few sunny days then, as the hay begins to dry, it will rain again. A few cycles of this kind of weather and the hay will rot on the ground. Oats do not grow well in this climate. They grow well in cool, northern climates. (2) You probably do not have the time and labor to raise your own oats and hay. You may have the climate, but do you have the time? Oats must be harvested at a certain stage - no sooner and no later. Hay must be raked and baled when it needs to be - too early and it will mold; too late and it will shatter and lose quality. Hay that must be baled does not wait for foaling mares, breeding, weaning or any of the chores and routines of the breeding farm. Most farms cannot afford to divert the staff necessary to rake, bale, load and unload hay. It is far less expensive to buy good hay and oats than it is to grow it yourself.

Buying an Existing Horse Farm: Buying an existing horse farm can be a good choice. The cost of developing new land, putting in roads and utilities and building barns and fences rises steadily. With an existing farm, it is likely that these improvements may be purchased for less money than they would cost you to build. Disregard the old idea of an existing farm being "horse-sick." Calumet and Greentree farms have had horses on them for decades and there are no finer places for raising racehorses.

Ask yourself several questions before buying someone else's horse farm. First, could I build a new farm - of equal quality - for less money than the purchase price of the existing farm? Most of the time the answer is no. Second, would I build a new farm with the same features as the existing farm? Or am I buying features and improvements I don't need? You may never use a training track, a second house on the farm or extensive office space. Since anything which is not used tends to suffer from neglect, you must consider if you want to pay for and maintain non-productive buildings and improvements.

Is the layout of the farm safe and efficient? Square corners in the pastures can be made round easily, but a new fence to separate all paddocks from the highway will be expensive. If the farm roads are inadequate or do not support tractors and large equipment, daily chores such as supplying hay and grain to the barns and removing the manure will be time-consuming. You will either have to put in new roads or put up with the inefficient layout. Remember, real estate costs are a one-time thing, but labor costs go on forever. Any savings on the purchase price could be eaten up quickly by higher labor costs. Safe and efficient farm layout is the subject of the next chapter.

Think twice before making an offer on a farm that is run down or neglected. If the barns are falling down and all the fences must be replaced, you will pay as much or more to restore the place as you would to build a new farm.

Investigate to make sure that the water and soil are free from contamination. You might assume that a tract of land is suitable because it has produced a variety of crops or sustained livestock in the past. But modern industrialization and development make this a hazardous assumption. Airborne pollutants, industrial runoff and contamination of ground water are all factors which may alter or ruin soil quality. Buried, leaking fuel tanks and old dump sites are common and hazardous. The problem is most contamination cannot be seen. Make every offer subject to an environmental inspection by an expert.

Converting Other Types of Farms: Another alternative to building is to convert another type of farm, such as a tobacco or dairy farm, into a horse farm. If the land is good and you are prepared to build new fences and renovate barns, this can be a good plan. It may allow you to take advantage of existing roads and utilities and, to a limited extent, existing buildings. But here again, ask yourself if you need everything you will be buying.

A tobacco farm is often the easiest to convert. Usually situated on good, rolling land, it often has many advantages and few undesirable features. Tobacco barns are tall and airy. Built to let the free movement of air dry the tobacco leaves, tobacco barns and sheds are healthy, if not fancy, structures for housing horses. And there are probably no other structures, such as silos and livestock pens, that must be torn down or removed. Most of your money for converting the tobacco farm can go directly into roads, fences and other improvements.

A dairy farm may also be converted to a horse farm. Dairy farms require a high-quality source of water and reliable electrical service, which can eliminate some steps of your development. Since milk is collected daily, the dairy farm probably has a good road in and out of it. A dairy barn is usually not suitable for horses, but it can be a good building for storing hay and straw. The outbuildings - every dairy farm has several - are useful for storing machinery and equipment. If you're prepared to build new barns, fences and additional roads, a dairy farm may be a good choice if you are sure that the land and water are still good. Don't pay for expensive silos or milking parlors that you cannot use.

A tobacco barn marks rich, fertile land. The barn may be converted to a horse farm, as this one has been.

(Photo courtesy of Martin Pierce)

Chapter 2

Horse Farm Layout

The arrangement of buildings, roads, paddocks and pastures determines whether your farm is efficient and safe. Before you begin to build anything, lay out your farm on a piece of paper. The expense of planning the proper layout is the best money you will ever spend.

You must design your farm with one overriding principle: *Every item of convenience is secondary to the safety of the horses.* If you violate this principle, sooner or later you will pay the price. This principle requires that several features be designed into the farm:

1. Vehicles and horses don't mix. All barns must be surrounded by fences to separate them from all parking and work areas. Horses have a way of escaping from their stalls or from their handlers. When this happens, no horse should ever be able to run on a road, a parking lot, a driveway or any area where machinery or tools are kept. It should be impossible for anyone to park a car anywhere on the farm and walk into a barn without first passing through a fence of some sort.

2. Horses also break out of their pastures and paddocks. To the extent possible, the fencing system should be designed so when this happens, a second fence stands between the horse and the roads, parking lot or work area. Ask yourself this question: "When the horse breaks free from the pasture, what options does he have?" The only acceptable options are to run into the barn or back into the paddock. If one of the options is to run into the parking area or any area where equipment is kept, you have a bad design.

3. The paddocks and pastures should be arranged so the horses can be turned out without first crossing a road or parking area. Horses need fences between themselves and vehicles at all times.

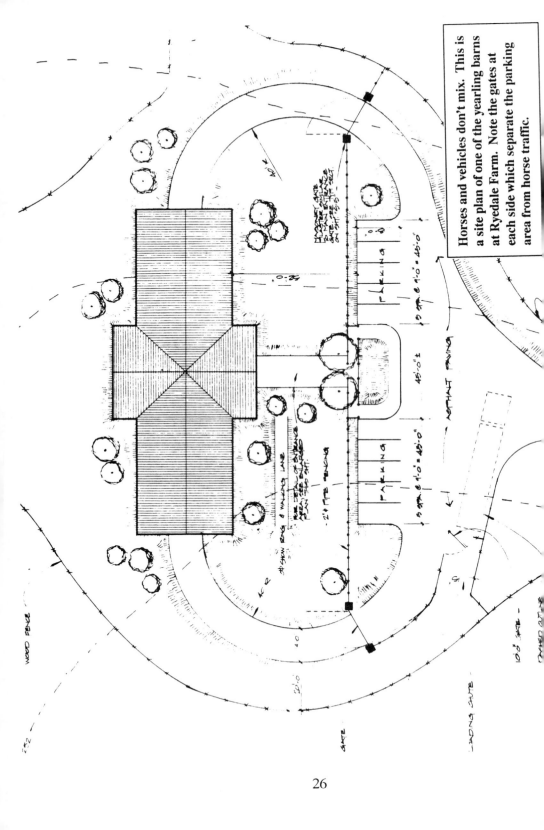

Horses and vehicles don't mix. This is a site plan of one of the yearling barns at Ryedale Farm. Note the gates at each side which separate the parking area from horse traffic.

26

Segmenting the Farm: Every large farm should be segmented into smaller tracts of about 80 acres each. Each 80-acre tract serves a single 20-stall barn, maintaining the 1:4 ratio of horses to acres which I mentioned earlier.

If your farm is only 40 or 80 acres, divide the farm into small tracts just as you would with a large farm. Do not build one large barn for all your horses. Instead of one 12-stall barn, build two six-stall barns. A very small operation may be served by two four-stall barns.

Placing 20-stall barns on individual 80-acre tracts lends itself to efficient management of the different types of horses living on the farm. Pregnant mares, barren mares, weanlings and yearlings each have different needs, requiring different types of management. You need to be able to segregate mares with foals from yearlings and yearling colts from yearling fillies. Good management is most efficiently accomplished by segmenting the farm.

There are other reasons for segmenting the farm. Any disease that enters the farm will go through an entire barn. A sick yearling necessarily quarantines his entire barn. Until the infection has run its course through the barn, its inhabitants must not be in contact with other horses in other barns. Employees must be able to care for the horses in the *sick barn* without even walking through any other barns or paddocks. Everyone must stay on their own unit if you are to avoid infecting every horse on the farm. By building 20-stall barns on individual 80-acre tracts, you isolate health problems.

Segmenting the farm makes individual tracts easier to sell if development approaches. Keep in mind that one of the benefits of farm ownership is the profitable use of the land until the day it is sold. Segmentation makes it easier to sell individual tracts without destroying the entire farm arrangement.

Location of Barns: All barns are built roughly in the center of the farm with separate paddocks and pastures easily accessible to each. The horses stalled in barn "A" always use the paddocks and pastures of the tract on which the barn is situated. They never use the paddocks and pastures on barn "B's" tract.

Roads: The road or driveway leading onto the farm from the main highway presents several design problems. Earlier I said that a farm should be so designed that when horses break free from their paddocks they cannot run onto a road. I also said that the farm should be designed so horses do not cross roads when being led to paddocks or pastures. How do you accomplish this?

Try to have the farm road run parallel to the property line as far as practical. The road then will branch off to serve various barns and other buildings on the farm. When it is not practical for the road to follow the property line, it must be designed to intersect with as few horse crossings as possible.

Usually, the road leading to each barn will cross some of the lanes leading to the surrounding pastures and paddocks. Special gates are constructed at these intersections. When the road is open to traffic, the gates close off the lanes. A horse escaping from a paddock or pasture is confined to the lane. When horses cross the road, the gate swings open from the lane and closes off the road. This keeps the horses from running onto the road and keeps vehicles away from the horses.

The design of a good horse barn is an entire topic by itself and is discussed in Chapter 5.

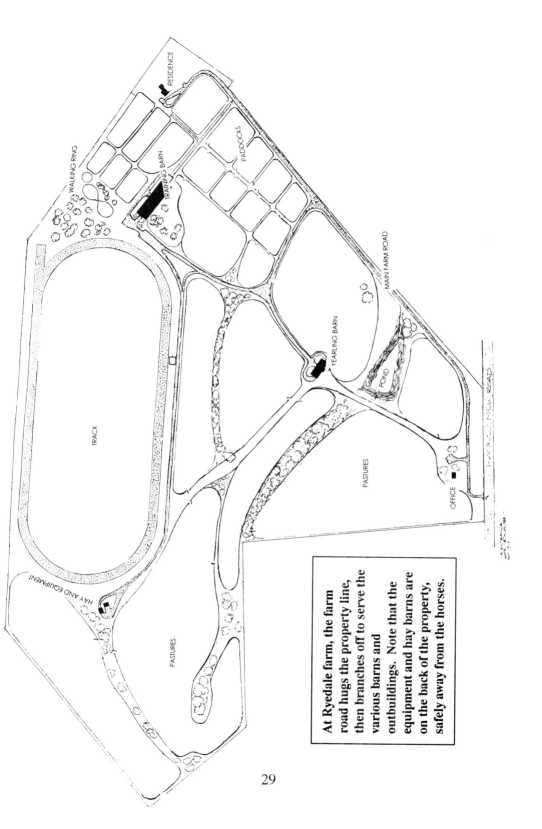

RESIDENCE

WALKING RING

TRAINING BARN

PADDOCKS

MAIN FARM ROAD

YEARLING BARN

TRACK

POND

PASTURES

OFFICE

HAY AND EQUIPMENT

PASTURES

At Ryedale farm, the farm road hugs the property line, then branches off to serve the various barns and outbuildings. Note that the equipment and hay barns are on the back of the property, safely away from the horses.

29

Special gates are erected wherever roads and lanes intersect. The gates swing two ways and close off either the road or the lane depending upon which is in use at the time. On any horse farm, horses always have the right-of-way. *(Photos courtesy of Suzie Oldham)*

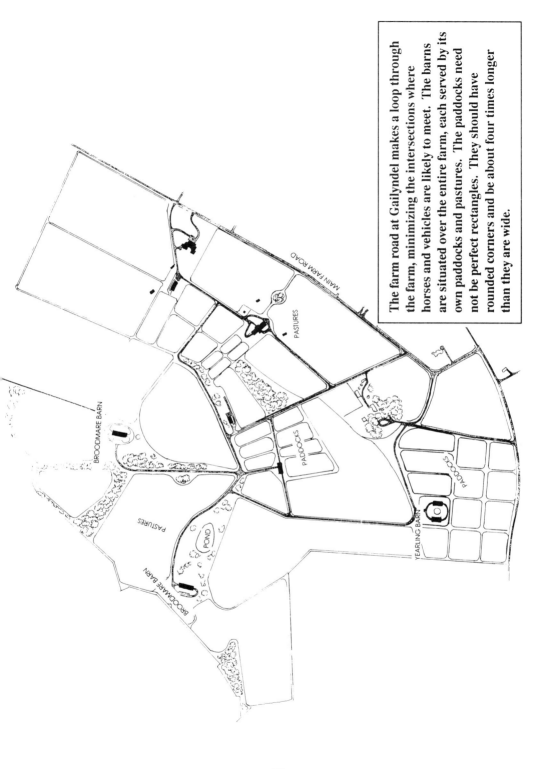

The farm road at Gailyndel makes a loop through the farm, minimizing the intersections where horses and vehicles are likely to meet. The barns are situated over the entire farm, each served by its own paddocks and pastures. The paddocks need not be perfect rectangles. They should have rounded corners and be about four times longer than they are wide.

MAIN FARM ROAD

PASTURES

BROODMARE BARN

PADDOCKS

PADDOCKS

YEARLING BARN

PASTURES

POND

BROODMARE BARN

31

Paddocks: Paddocks are built immediately adjacent to the barns. Paddocks are used to turn out stallions, sale yearlings, broodmares with newborn foals and horses that for one reason or another cannot be put in the pasture with the other horses.

For yearlings, you will need one paddock for every two stalls in the barn. An arrangement of 10 paddocks and two pastures per 20-stall barn is a workable distribution. Broodmares need fewer paddocks but more pasture space. Five paddocks are sufficient for a broodmare barn.

A good size for a paddock is about 2 1/2 acres. The ideal shape is four times longer than it is wide. A paddock that is 20 posts wide should be about 80 posts long. This size will give a colt enough room to run and kick up his heels without presenting a danger to himself.

Paddocks don't have to be laid out in perfect rectangles. They can be odd shapes. The layout should follow the contours of the land.

I don't like trees in my paddocks. Horses can run into them and injure themselves. Build the fences so the trees are outside the paddock. This may result in some oddly shaped paddocks, but that is not important. Odd shapes can add interest to the farm layout and the horses don't seem to mind.

(Photo courtesy of Suzie Oldham)

Position fences at the top of hills so as horses approach the fence, they are running uphill. Fences should never be located at the bottom of hills where horses can approach them running downhill. Placing the fence at the bottom of the hill effectively lowers the height of the fence. The horse might be tempted to jump over. A stretch of flat ground between the hill and the fence is needed for the horse to gauge his speed and his distance from the fence so he can stop safely.

I don't like trees in my paddock, but sometimes this is not practical. You may have a clump of beautiful trees that you cannot fence out. In that case, build a fence around them. Build the fence far enough away from the trees so the horses cannot reach over the top and chew off the bark. I like to keep the bottom board off the ground about one foot so a mower will fit under it or grazing sheep or cattle can reach under it. One foot of clearance also allows horses to graze a bit under the fence without becoming trapped.

Trees that cannot be fenced out of a paddock or pasture must be protected by fencing. *(Photo courtesy of Suzie Oldham)*

The corners of all paddock fences are curved or arced. There should be no right-angle corners in a paddock. Horses frequently gallop along the fence lines. If they are going at a full gallop, they might not be able to stop when they come up to an intersecting fence. When the paddock corners are curved, the horse is guided safely around the turn.

Do not put sharp corners in a paddock. The corners should be curved. *(Photo courtesy of Suzie Oldham)*

Paddocks must not share a common fence. There must be an eight- to 12-foot lane between paddocks. Eight feet is the minimum safe distance and twelve feet is ideal. Trees can help to separate the paddocks. I like a lane to have four feet of grass on either side of a four-foot-wide planting of trees. These dimensions make it easy to get a mower down the lanes. The trees present an effective screen between horses, blocking the line of sight between the paddocks. Horses always seem to want to join the horse in the paddock next to them. The wide lane and the screen of trees discourage "fraternization" between paddocks.

Separate stallion paddocks with 12-foot lanes between them, too. But a larger space is needed between the stallion paddocks and all other pastures and paddocks. A 50-foot lane or a road with trees alongside is required to prevent stallions from seeing mares or any other horses except stallions. If a lane rather than a road is used, you need a 12- to 14-foot-wide row of trees, shrubs or hedges to block the view. A dense screen of vegetation is absolutely necessary if the paddocks are to hold stallions.

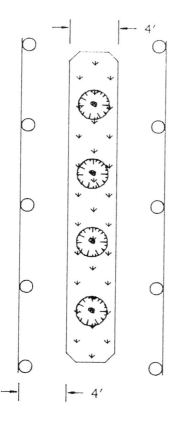

Four feet of trees with four feet of grass on either side makes a good lane between paddocks.

Pastures: Pastures lie beyond the paddocks. Many horses will be turned out together and each pasture must be large enough to allow each one to graze freely and to escape from the more aggressive leaders of the herd. A pasture of 15, 20, 30 or more acres is not too large. Occasionally, when the land is available, pastures of even 100 acres can be justified.

A general rule is four horses for 15 to 20 acres and six horses per 30-acre field. The only hard and fast rule is never overcrowd a pasture.   Proper pasture size depends on the horses using it. Broodmares with foals are turned out four pairs to a 20-acre pasture. After weaning, you may put 15 weanlings in a 30-acre field. Up to 20 mares recently separated from their foals may use a 100-acre field while their regular pasture receives maintenance.

Like paddocks, pastures are laid out to follow the contours of the land. They need not be perfect rectangles. In almost all cases, odd shapes are preferable. Fences belong at the top of hills, not the bottom. Corners should be curved.

Unlike paddocks, trees are an asset in large pastures. Large trees or clumps of trees provide shade for the horses on hot summer days but they need protection from horses gnawing on them. An excellent solution for this is discussed in the chapter on pastures.

Waterers: Each pasture and paddock needs its own water supply. A large pasture may need two waterers.

The location of the waterer is important. Horses like to congregate in one area of the pasture, usually along a fence somewhere near the gate. In doing so, they can create an awful mess. The grass gets trampled to the point that it will no longer grow. In the rainy season, the area becomes a sea of mud. While it may not be possible to eliminate this habit, there is no need to encourage it. That's why I put my waterers in the middle of the pasture, not along the fence line or near gates. The chance of a horse being injured with the waterer in the middle of the field is a lot less than if it is near a fence. And, the need for the horse to walk to the middle of the pasture to get a drink is good exercise.

To provide fresh drinking water in sub-zero temperatures, you need a waterer that won't freeze, doesn't require above-ground wires or extension cords and is designed so it that cannot injure the horses. The waterer I like is a *Nelson*™ waterer. This is a cone-shaped, heavy concrete fountain with an aluminum top that is heated electrically in the winter. Water is supplied by underground pipe. The electric line leading to it is buried in the same trench as the water line. Use conduit to protect the electric line from breaking or shorting out during periods of freezing and thawing. The pipe must be deep enough to remain below the frost line in the severest weather and the wiring must be heavy enough for the distance covered.

Waterers should have a removable "catch pan" for easy cleaning. The horse drinks from a shallow aluminum basin that lifts out, just as the top pan lifts out of a double boiler. There must be no sharp edges or protrusions to injure a horse. Waterers must be stable so a horse cannot knock them over. *(Photo courtesy of Suzie Oldham)*

Run-in Sheds: Back in the 1950s, run-in sheds were popular for housing broodmares and young horses. They were said to be an easy, natural way of keeping horses, so I put run-in sheds in all my pastures. They were out in the open, with no fences around them. I always hoped the horses would volunteer to go inside the sheds in bad weather, but they never did. Whenever a storm came, I'd go to see where the horses were and I would always find them on a hill somewhere, hindquarters pointed into the wind. I'd call them and feed them inside the shed, trying to keep them inside until the storm passed. But this was rarely successful - as soon as they heard a noise they would get scared and run outside. They just weren't comfortable in there.

I noticed a lot of jostling and kicking going on while horses were inside the sheds. It was difficult for a timid horse to avoid an aggressive pasture-mate in the confines of the run-in shed. This made me uncomfortable, so I changed my policy. To suit the horses' desire to live outside, I keep them in the pastures and paddocks, keeping them inside only during inclement weather.

You don't need a run-in shed. If the weather is so bad that the horses need shelter, bring them into the barn. The barn is safer than a shed, since they can't chase and kick each other while in their stalls. Good management will save you the expense of building run-in sheds.

Houses: To my way of thinking, there is no better place to build a home than on the farm itself. The major consideration in selecting a site for your house is the setting. Select a site with the best view, a place where you can look out over the farm. The only restriction is that the location of your house and the drive leading to it must not complicate the operation of the farm.

Design the house so the grazing horses are part of the landscape. Sitting outdoors on a warm summer night watching the mares and foals graze nearby is one of life's great pleasures. Friends that come to visit are always delighted by the scene. It is said that Leslie Combs built Spendthrift Farm on this philosophy. He would invite prospective buyers to the farm for dinner. As the guests dined, the mares and foals would graze along the fence line outside the dining room window. Leaving nothing to chance, he had sprinkled grain on the ground in just the right place to attract the horses and to afford his guests the most pleasant view. The guests all went home horse owners. You can do the same.

Sheds and Outbuildings: The horse farm requires three separate storage areas: one for hay and straw, one for equipment and one to store the muck from the stalls. Plan the layout of your farm so all hay and straw storage, machinery storage and manure pits are located together toward the back of the farm, away from horse traffic and visitors. There must be a good system of roads around these facilities because they are used daily. This requires good planning but is the safest and most efficient layout.

Hay and straw must not be stored in the horse barn. It creates dust which leads to respiratory problems and is a fire hazard. A separate storage building is needed. A hay storage building doesn't have to be new. An old barn may work well. The only requirements are that it keep the hay dry and be accessible. Horse barns must be resupplied daily with hay and straw and new shipments will arrive regularly.

Tractors, lawnmowers, weedeaters, welders and other machinery need a separate storage building. This is a safety requirement. Machinery requires gasoline or other flammable fuels and there is always the possibility of stray sparks. Never store equipment in the same building as your hay and never store it near horses.

You need a place to store muck from the stalls until it can be picked up and hauled away. If you use dumpsters, place them in the back of the farm.

Manure Pits: A manure pit is an excellent way of storing the muck that accumulates from the stalls. The best manure pit is dug into the ground, with the floor and three walls lined with concrete. The muck is easily unloaded each day and easy to haul away. The in-ground design keeps it from blowing around and making a mess. The concrete floor and sides allow a man with a front-end loader to scoop up the manure quite efficiently. You don't need someone standing there raking and shoveling it in. It will cost a little to construct this, but you'll make up the expense in labor saved. It is easier to sell or give away the muck to mushroom growers or mulch suppliers if it can be easily loaded and hauled away.

Co-mingling Horses and Other Livestock: In Europe, you often see sheep grazing alongside horses. It makes a charming picture and the sheep have a calming effect on the horses. Sheep also have the useful habit of eating the grass around and under the fences that horses can't reach. Cattle can also be grazed alongside horses if they are polled (dehorned). Cattle serve the horse breeder best in late summer and fall when they eat the grass that has grown too tall and coarse to be palatable to horses. The parasites of sheep and cattle do not affect horses. They may be grazed in horse pastures without contaminating the grass for horses.

If you decide to co-mingle horses with sheep or cattle, introduce the other livestock slowly and carefully. Most American horses never have seen a sheep or a cow and will react with fear. Putting a yearling into a paddock with a calf may cause the colt to run through the fence. Introduce one or two animals at a time and from a distance of two or three paddocks. Leave the cow or sheep in the distant paddock for a week while the horses note its smells and watch how it moves. After a week, put the cow or sheep in a paddock next to the horses. If the horses remain calm and you wish to add a second animal, do it now. After a day or two, lead the pair of sheep or cattle to the horses' paddock and watch the expressions of the horses. If they react with calm curiosity, go ahead with your plan. But if they show any fear, take the other livestock back to their own paddock and try again in another week. The care you take introducing cattle or sheep to the horses will pay dividends later on, when these livestock exert their calming effect on your horses.

One special warning - keep all dogs away from your horses. Dogs are usually a menace around horses and the problem is compounded when there are cattle and sheep to chase. A chasing dog can provoke a real stampede and you may have horses running through fences - expensive entertainment for the dog. Keep the dogs at home.

Chapter 3

Fences, Gates & Latches

Good fences should keep the horses confined, be safe and contribute to the overall beauty of the farm. In my opinion, the best horse fence is the traditional, four-board, wood variety.

Fence Height: I build my paddock fences 5 1/2 feet high and my pasture fences five feet high. The extra six inches in the paddocks makes a big difference when you are trying to keep yearlings fenced in. The extra height makes it less tempting for them to try and jump over it.

Fence Posts: Most fence posts are 7 1/2 feet high, which is fine for pasture fencing. This allows five feet above the ground and 2 1/2 feet in the ground. Since paddock fences are 1/2 foot higher, you will need eight foot fence posts to give you the 5 1/2 foot paddock fence.

The best-sized fence post is 4 1/2 to six inches in diameter. Because they must be pressure-treated to withstand rotting, I prefer the posts that are about 4 1/2 to five inches in diameter. While a six inch post may look better, the 4 1/2 to five inch posts actually last longer because they are easier to treat. The chemicals penetrate more thoroughly through the smaller post. A properly treated post should last about 20 years. The posts are usually pine but any good, treated post will work. If you can find black locust posts, buy them. Black locust posts will last 20 years without any treatment.

Boards: The best fence boards are made of oak. Make them one inch thick, six inches wide and 16 feet long. A good quality oak board does not need to be treated. Oak boards will last about 20 years, the same as the treated posts. There is no substitute for oak boards. Other woods, such as pine, lack strength for the punishment that horses will give. The softer pine board splinters when it breaks. The large slivers can seriously injure a horse if they are driven deep into the flesh. This will not happen with oak.

Batten Strips: A batten strip is a vertical board nailed over the fence rails to keep the rails snug to the posts. While they give a neat appearance, I do not use batten strips on my fences. My experience is that they cause the rails to rot at the point they are attached to the posts and they are often knocked loose by mowers. Since the batten strip is fastened to the post with eight nails, which can protrude or fall into the pasture, a loose one is a dangerous thing.

The only place I don't mind batten strips or boards is on the second or outside fence that borders the road. Since horses do not come in contact with this fence, it may be constructed for looks only.

Basic Construction: The fence posts are spaced eight feet on center. The posts are placed into holes about 2 1/2 feet deep. With a good treated post, you will not have to put gravel or any material other than dirt in the post hole. The horse fence has no corners, only curves. A four-board, wood fence is self-supporting, requiring no special support or bracing. The boards are nailed to the posts, usually using nail guns which do the job quickly. However, these nails are not as good a #8 galvanized nail. When a board comes loose, I like to use the traditional coated nail to repair it.

Construct the fence so the boards are nailed on the inside of the fence, the side that faces the horses. If the fence is built with the boards on the outside, the posts will be jutting into the pastures or paddocks. Since horses frequently run along the fence line, they are likely to strike a knee on a post if the fence is built with the boards on the outside. Occasionally, an owner will build the fence "wrong side out," with the boards toward the road so it looks a bit better. It seems that a horse can find a way to injure itself standing still in the middle of a 40-acre field. The problems caused by one knee banged against a post don't justify the slight improvement in appearance of a fence improperly built. Don't build safety hazards into your fences.

Set the top rail of the fence 1/4 to 1/2 inch below the top of the fence post. Place the bottom rail 14 inches off the ground to allow clearance to get a weed eater under it. Place the second board six inches above the bottom one and the third board seven inches above the second. The top board goes eight inches above the third. If you are building a three-board fence, you may raise up the bottom rail a bit to about 18 inches.

Saw the top of the post at a slight angle to allow water to run off. Make the cut so the post is highest where it meets the board and slopes down to the outside of the fence. This is easily done with a chainsaw. You won't accidently cut the boards if you have placed them 1/4 to 1/2 inch below the fence post.

This drawing shows the specifications of the four-board fence.
(Illustration courtesy of Judy Hanson)

You are using 16-foot boards nailed onto posts eight feet apart. Stagger the boards so every post will have the ends of two boards and the middle of two others. A stronger, safer fence results when all the boards do not end on the same post.

Building good horse fencing is a big job which usually can be done better for less cost by professionals. Large fence companies have hydraulic rams which drive the posts directly into the ground without the need to dig a post hole. They are amazing machines which drive the posts right through bedrock. The machines set the posts at the required depth. You will only lose about an inch of post as you saw them off at a slant. The cost of building a good quality, four-board fence, including painting, is about $15,000 a mile.

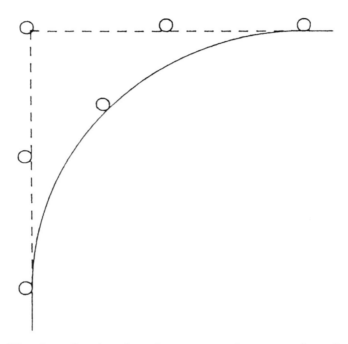

The above drawing shows how to curve the corners for safety.

Painting Fences: I've seen people paint their fences pink, green, gray and almost every other color. But the two most popular colors are white and black. A white fence makes a farm look manicured. It points it to being in the high rent district. But my favorite is a black fence.

The difference between a white and black fence is in the maintenance. The black paint has an asphalt base with lots of fiber in it. I use *Kentucky Ranch Paint*™ but I am sure that there are other good brands out there. The paint is sprayed on the fence. Two men on opposite sides of the fence wield spray guns from a large power sprayer and tank. It's a fast process. They can do the same with white paint. The problem comes several years later when you repaint the fence. Black, asphalt-based paint lets you spray right over the first coat because it doesn't flake or peel. Before repainting a white fence, you must scrape off the first coat, which has turned into a flaking, peeling eyesore. This is time-consuming and costly.

Most horses like to chew on wood, especially the cribbers. The black asphalt paint discourages wood chewing for the first year or 18 months. After that, one horse will find a place to start chewing and finds that it doesn't taste too bad. Soon others follow his lead. There is no good way to stop horses from chewing on the fence except to put an electric wire across the top board. If you balk at this idea, the only thing to do is to replace the boards that have been chewed.

Diamond Mesh Fences: Another excellent type of fence for horses is the *Diamond Mesh*™ fence. This fence consists of a single board along the top and diamond mesh wire between the top board and the ground. The same fence posts are used as with the four-board fence and are set eight feet on center. It's a safe fence, in some ways safer than a four-board plank fence.

The problem is that a Diamond Mesh fence is more expensive, harder to build and harder to take around the turns when you put your posts on the outside of the pasture or paddock. The tension required to keep the wire tight will tend to pull the fence posts toward the inside of the pasture. Even if the posts are rock-steady, the wire pulls against the staples and loosens them in time. Most horses will discover a sagging section of fence and will injure themselves in the time it takes to tell about it. One solution is to build the straight stretches of the fence with wire and the turns with the traditional four boards. The straight sections should be five feet high and the four-board turns, 5 1/2 feet high.

To build a *Diamond Mesh*™ fence, a "pull" post must be installed every 80 feet. A pull post is used to pull the wire tight and anchor it. A pull post is nine inches in diameter instead of the usual 5 1/2 inches or six inches and is nine feet long. Pull posts are placed in post holes 3 1/2 feet deep which are filled with concrete to a point about 12 inches below the ground surface. The concrete also extends

12 inches around the base of the post and four feet out in each direction that the wire is pulling. This 4-foot concrete ledge provides a brace against the wire which is constantly pulling against the post.

This is a Diamond Mesh™ wire fence, a safe alternative to traditional four-board fences. Note the large pull post in the foreground. *(Photo courtesy of Martin Pierce)*

It is important to keep the concrete at least 12 inches below the ground surface for several reasons. You do not want the horses to step on this concrete slab or strike it with a hoof. Horses naturally run up and down fence lines, creating a ditch along the fence. Set the concrete far enough into the ground so that as the surrounding turf is worn away, a dangerous slab of concrete is not exposed. If you don't keep the concrete deep into the ground, you soon have an area for a horse to injure a hoof, cut a coronet or damage a pastern.

Installing pull posts is a slow process. The wire must be tight between pull posts, which will bear the majority of the stress of the wire as it wants to recoil. Each end of the wire roll is wrapped around a post and tied off neatly. The wire is stapled to all posts, using 1 1/2-inch staples on each mesh. This requires a lot of staples, but it is necessary for a tight, safe fence. All loose, ragged wire must be trimmed off. Properly done, the result is a safe, neat fence.

Diamond mesh can be used around turns in a horse fence if it is wired to the post. After the mesh is stapled to the post, take #9 wire and thread it through the mesh and around the post, tying the wire to the fence post. Tie the wire to the post every six inches, all the way to the top of the mesh.

Electric Fences and Barb Wire Fences: I don't like electric fences or barbed wire fences. A galloping horse cannot see a thin, electric wire stretched between two posts. Horses, especially yearlings, will run right through them. The danger presented by barb wire fences is obvious. If you use barb wire, you are asking for trouble.

Plastic Fencing: There are many brands of plastic fencing available. I think they are probably good, safe alternatives to the traditional board fences. They have a lot of give to them if a horse hits them. After they're installed, there's very little maintenance. But I think they're going to cost you about three times as much as the four-board fence I have described.

Eliminating Slop at Gate Entrances: A problem on every horse farm is the mud and slop which accumulates at gate entrances. When the gate entrance gets wet, the hooves of the horses churn the sod into mud. Not only is it a mess, but it detracts from the beauty of the pasture or paddock. To cure the problem, you must first understand the cause of the problem.

There are two conditions which lead to the formation of mud at the gate, both of which deal with drainage. Frequently, gates are located in a naturally low area or at the base of a hill or incline. Water runs down from the higher ground and out under the gate. The second condition is created by horses congregating at the gate. No matter how hard you try to break them of the habit, horses tend to gather at the gate about the time they know they will be brought into the barn. The weight of the horses packs down the ground and creates a depression which is several inches lower than the surrounding ground. Water then collects in the entrance and the traffic of the horses grinds the turf into mud.

The solution is to place the gate entrance at the highest point possible. Keep the entrance out of swales and low areas. Make sure the surrounding land is lower than the point at which the entrance is placed. Don't build your entrance at a point where the water will naturally drain under the gate.

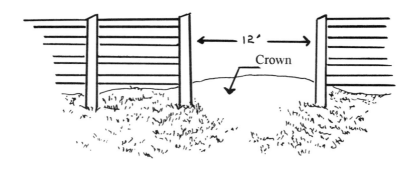

"Crowning" the area leading under gates will allow water to run off, eliminating the mud which usually accumulates here.
(Illustration courtesy of Judy Hanson)

Next, it is important to build a good base at the gate entrances. Place No. 2 rock in the area to a depth of about two feet. Over the top of the stone, place a layer of lime dust. Crown the entire entrance area so the center is higher than the sides. Use the same strategy a road builder does. All roads are built higher in the center so the water runs off to either side. Your gate entrance should be built the same way, with a crown to it. The crown should begin about 12 to 15 feet into the pasture and continue out under the gate for about another four feet.

Gate entrances can be maintained every few years by putting down a layer of sawdust or tanbark over the built-up area. This helps maintain the area, absorbs moisture and makes a safe footing for horses. Be careful not to destroy the elevation of the crown when you put down the sawdust or tanbark.

Gates Made of Pipe: In my opinion, the best gates are made from lightweight, 2-inch steel pipe. I have them fabricated for me by a local welder. My steel pipe gates consist of four horizontal pipes supported by a vertical pipe on either side and two more vertical pipes in the middle. The horizontal pipes are spaced at about the same distance as if you were building a four-board fence. The four corners are rounded. All welds are smoothed so no rough or ragged edges remain.

All gates need a footrest to help support the weight of the gate while it is in a closed position. The footrest is placed level with the bottom of the gate so it is necessary to lift the gate slightly to set it on the footrest. Using the footrest prolongs the life of the hinges.

(Photo courtesy of Martin Pierce)

Pipe gates look good, they hold up well and are safe. If a horse puts a foot through the gate, he can withdraw it easily because the pipe is round. This gate also has no narrow spaces or "V"s that can trap a horse's foot. There are only the two vertical pipes, well-spaced, that form 90 degree angles with the horizontal pipes, so the horse cannot get his hoof stuck. If a horse tries to jump a pipe gate, he will slide right over the round pipes. A wooden gate usually breaks under an unsuccessful jump, often injuring the horse. Pipe gates last many years, making them more economical than wooden gates which only last for about five years.

Gate Width and Swing: The best width for a gate is 12 feet. A 12-foot-wide gate allows mowers, chain harrows and other equipment to go through it. If you make the opening narrower, say eight or 10 feet, you will have problems getting equipment through the opening and you'll always be hitting the gate posts.

Gates should swing out of the paddocks or pastures, not into them. In other words, gates should swing away from the confined horses, not toward them. If the wind takes a gate that opens to the inside, it could swing into a horse and cause the horse to panic. Every gate needs a "stop" which limits the gate's swing. This way, if the gate gets away from you it swings only as far as the stop, which may be as simple as a tree in the lane. A gate that opens inside the paddock cannot have a stop. A gate without a stop soon damages its hinges.

Mount the hinges and the latch on the center of the gate posts. They should sit in line with the fence, neither inside nor outside the fence. The stop will prevent the gate from catching on the post when it is completely open.

There are two circumstances where a gate that opens inside is acceptable. If your terrain rises sharply, the gate that swings outside might not have clearance to open far enough. The land forces you to swing the gate inside. A gate which swings to the inside can be used if you have only one horse, preferably not a yearling, to turn out and bring in from the paddock. If the horse is quiet and allows you to lead him and control the gate with your other hand, a gate that swings inside is satisfactory.

A gate that swings inside needs its hinges mounted on the inside. Set the hinges on the pasture or paddock side of the post so the gate is able to swing fully open against the fence rails. You cannot put the hinges on the center of the post because as the gate swings back toward the fence, it will catch against the hinge post and break the gate or loosen the hinges.

Install the gate four inches higher than the rest of the fence. The extra height is a safety factor. All horses know that the gate is the way out of the paddock and an excited or insecure yearling may try to jump out. Even weanlings, long after being weaned, may attempt to scramble over a gate. Horses are much less tempted to jump a gate that is higher than the fence.

The gate that is four inches higher than the fence encourages the horse to "put on the brakes." *(Photo courtesy of Martin Pierce)*

Slam Posts: One way to stop a gate from opening a full 180 degrees against the fence is to use a slam post. A slam post doesn't have to be as large as a regular gate post because its only function is to stop the gate. Make a slam post by ripping halfway through a fence post, down to the level of the bottom of the gate. The gate swings into the ripped out section and rests on the entire piece of post below. A fence post with a chock attached to the bottom at the height of the bottom of the gate serves as a slam post, too.

Gate Posts: Gate posts are of two types: hinge posts, which must be heavy enough to support the entire weight of the gate, and latch posts. A nine-foot-long post that is nine inches in diameter is a good size for the hinge post. The post to which the gate latches is a standard size post.

Start with the hinge post, setting it 3 1/2 feet into the ground. Pour concrete around the base, as a brace, to a depth of one foot below the surface. When the hinge post for your 12-foot gate is set, mount the gate. After the gate is mounted on its hinges, set the post that has the latches. Don't set both the hinge and latch posts, then try to put the gate on - chances are it won't fit right. The order is hinge post first, gate, then latch post.

A slam post preserves the gate's hinges.
(Photo courtesy of Martin Pierce)

52

Automatic Gates: Automatic gates are gates that open by themselves from an electrical signal, either from pressing a button or triggered from an electric eye. With an automatic gate, it is not necessary to leave your vehicle to open it. They are most often used in farm entrances and driveways.

Automatic gates have a reputation for being troublesome and requiring frequent repairs. In my opinion, this is undeserved. Automatic gates will operate perfectly for years if they are installed correctly. The gate must be balanced and the electronic components and motor must be hooked up by a technician who understands how the gate works. It is not a job for you or a self-taught handyman.

Slat Gates: The most dangerous gate for horses is a slat gate. This gate is sold at ranch or farm stores and is made of lightweight metal. It has a brace that runs from the top corner of one side to the bottom corner on the opposite side. A "V" is created at the point where the brace connects with the side of the gate. The problem with this gate is that horses can place their hooves through the gate and catch them in the "V". When his hoof is caught, the horse will panic and try to rip

A slat gate is a dangerous gate. A horse can put his hoof into this gate, causing him to panic and injure himself.

(Photo courtesy of Judy Hanson)

53

it free. The ensuing struggle will seriously injure the horse and will destroy the gate. You may get tired of my saying it, but horses will injure themselves standing still. Don't engineer safety hazards into your farm.

Double Swinging Gates: Double swinging gates are used to close a farm road or driveway to horse traffic. These gates are 14 feet wide and made from pipe. Because the length adds weight, double swinging gates must be hung from sturdy hinges.

Double swinging gates close off a large area, such as an entrance or farm road. *(Photo courtesy of Suzie Oldham)*

Gate Latches: A hook is a safe latch. A chain is a safe way of keeping the gate closed, too. A deadbolt latch is a poor choice because the bolt can protrude and catch the horse's flesh.

Having two means of securing a gate is another safety factor. A gate that has a latch and a chain is less apt to be left open accidently. The chain not only helps you to remember to close the gate and keep the horses safely inside, it lengthens the useful life of the gate. (A gate left open for one stormy night in March suffers a lifetime of use.)

A strong, safe gate latch that I devised is shown here. Notice that nothing protrudes to hurt the horse if he should bump against the gate or post.

(RLM photo)

The latch opens easily with one hand. When you have a fresh colt on your hands, you don't want to fiddle with difficult gate latches.

(Photo courtesy of Suzie Oldham)

The spring handle is mounted on the gate and fits securely into the bracket on the post. It looks neat, is simple to use and we haven't had a horse figure out how to open it yet.   *(RLM photo)*

We use this latch on main gates around the farm. The gate is secured between the two triangular catches of the latch. The angled bar on the bottom of the latch directs the gate's pin into position.

(Photo courtesy of Suzie Oldham)

Pulling the ring upward releases the catch and allows the gate to open. Releasing the ring closes the latch. Notice how this latch is mounted flat against the post. A horse cannot injure himself if he brushes against it.

(Photo courtesy of Martin Pierce)

Hinges: Hinges for horse gates have always interested me, perhaps because I see so many bad hinges on horse farms. Because they must be strong to support the sturdy gates required on horse farms yet free of protruding edges or bolts, they pose certain engineering problems. I have examined hinges all across the United States and in my travels to Europe and I have selected one particular hinge as superior to all others. The best hinge is a pipe/sleeve design. The vertical pipe of the hinge side of the gate fits into larger pipes at the top and bottom. A two-inch pipe attached to the gate fits inside a 2 1/4 or 2 1/2 inch piece of pipe (depending on the gauge of the pipe). These larger pieces of pipe are fastened to the gate post with a metal collar. The gate pipe turns inside the larger pipes at top and bottom. The collar remains stationary on the gate post which is not weakened by bolts or by the torque of a large gate. The gate pipe has a grease fitting where it fits inside the larger pipe. With regular lubrication, once or twice a year, this hinge will last for decades.

Don't put lag screws through the gate posts - they weaken the wood. Use pipes to construct a sleeve to fit over the posts. A pipe hinge lasts for years without sagging, which also preserves the gate post.

(Photo courtesy of Suzie Oldham)

Chapter 4

Pastures

Good pasture is the best source of nutrition for horses. Properly sown and maintained, a pasture will last for 20 years or more. It's a big investment, so don't cheat yourself by taking shortcuts.

Good horse grass is actually a mixture of grasses. We use bluegrass mixed with orchard grass, timothy, fescue and a little clover. A good ratio is 50% - 60% bluegrass, 5% clover and the balance in timothy, orchard grass and fescue. Each type of grass supplies varied amounts of protein, vitamins, fiber, calcium, phosphorus and other minerals necessary for good horse nutrition.

There is some controversy about fescue possibly causing abortions, but I think fescue is much maligned. We use a hybrid fescue that is superior to the old "31" used years ago and I've never had a problem with it. It's a land builder. It stops erosion and maintains the topsoil. You don't use too much of it but properly planted and mowed, it's a real asset. It's sweet, it has a nice big leaf and the horses love it after the fall frost.

Establishing Pastures: Establishing a pasture is a four-step process: (1) Select the location according to natural features and accessibility to the barns (discussed in Chapter One, *Finding the Right Land*). Plan to put your pastures in before the fences are built. It is much easier and cheaper to work the land without having to maneuver around and alongside expensive four-board fences. Plan to have the first three steps of this process completed by early fall. Fall is the best time to plant the seed for your pastures; (2) plow and level the area. You're not trying to move mountains or take the roll out, but level the ditches, gullies and low spots. Remove any swales or low areas where water can collect; (3) test the soil and fertilize accordingly before you plant. Well-fertilized soil will support your grass and your horses. It will help the pasture "take hold" sooner and it will help it last longer; and, (4) seed the land heavily in the fall, September in moderate climates such as Kentucky. You're not going to seed it like the feed store tells you unless you want to wait three years for your pasture. Plan to use two or three times the recommended amount of seed. Sixty pounds of seed per acre is not too much to establish a good, strong pasture. A cover crop is not absolutely necessary. If you put one in, plant it thinly. The goal is to establish a pasture, not to harvest rye or oats. Early the following spring, in February or whenever they start the plant beds in your country, seed it back again. Use a drill to drill more seed back into any thin areas that have frozen out over the winter. This reinforces any spots that didn't catch the first time or washed out during the winter.

It usually takes about 18 months to establish a pasture that you can feel good about. If you do everything right and the weather is with you, you might even have horses grazing on that pasture in a year.

Pasture Maintenance: Maintain the pasture by keeping it fertilized, mowed and rested. Test the soil in every pasture and paddock each fall. Take samples from different areas of the pasture, four or five samples for a 40-acre field. The results will show that samples taken from a rich stand of grass differ from those taken in a bare spot. The difference will help illustrate what the pasture needs. It may need a little phosphate or lime or nitrogen, depending on how much leaches out. As soon as trucks can be driven into the pastures in the spring, apply the necessary fertilizer.

A key to maintaining the quality of a pasture or paddock is to mow it regularly. Keep the grass about six inches high. Grass this height has a good balance of moisture, protein and fiber. Mowing it regularly keeps the seed heads from forming. Extremely tall, coarse grass is unpalatable to horses and if it's gone to seed, the nutritional value is diminished. Regular mowing is also a means of controlling weeds in a pasture.

Pasture that resembles a golf course, with short, tender grass, presents another problem. This grass is full of moisture and horses love it. But extremely short grass lacks fiber. You *must* supplement this pasture with hay to avoid colic. You may even need to limit the turnout time until the grass grows taller and becomes coarser.

Every 10 days to two weeks is about the right schedule for mowing, assuming adequate rainfall. Dry weather means less mowing. Grass cut at proper intervals will produce only light clippings that will burn up in the sun. Wet or voluminous clippings are dangerous because they can mold or ferment. In this situation, keep horses off the area until the clippings are thoroughly dried.

I use rotary mowers, but I'm not saying that they're the best. They're definitely cheaper and easier to use. But I think that a sickle or cutter bar mower is better. Sickle bar mowers won't bruise the grass and don't tear up the leaves as much. The big disadvantage to them is that it's difficult to mow high enough. You usually have to set a sickle bar mower pretty low. But if you are able to raise the blades and get them extremely sharp, they'll do the best job.

Pastures must be rested from time-to-time throughout the season. Horses are hard on pastures. They will run them down and trample them until the grass is bare. Short pasture is vulnerable to weeds, too. Watch for signs of this happening. A week or two of rest and a little rain will restore most areas.

Even pastures and paddocks that look fine should be rested occasionally. It strengthens them and controls parasites. I like to take the mares and foals off a pasture or paddock in the fall and leave it open until the next spring. The new foals will go out on a clean pasture and you will feel good about that. Rest the paddocks every eighth week for at least one week. This will really freshen up the grass.

Thin spots and hard areas need periodic reseeding. You'll need to add dirt to some of the bare spots. A truckload is usually enough for a paddock. Spread the dirt around and seed it, then cover it with straw. Given a couple months rest, it will come back nicely. It is ideal to rest the newly seeded area for six months.

Harrowing: Harrowing is an important tool for pasture management. When you harrow a pasture, you accomplish three things: (1) You kill parasites by breaking up the piles of manure. The sun will dry and kill the larvae if the fecal balls are broken up and spread out. (2) You return nutrients to the soil. Some of the minerals in the dry grass and manure will be put back into the pasture. (3) You prevent the build-up of roughs. Piles of manure will cause the grass under and around them to become rank and sour. Horses won't eat it. If you ignore the piles of manure, the horses will turn part of your expensive pasture into a "rough" or horse bathroom. Harrowing prevents this from happening. Harrow all pastures four to five times a year.

A pasture harrow looks like a piece of chain link fence. It is actually a specially made piece of equipment with spikes that tear up the manure and break up any thatch. It will leave stripes across a field, showing where it was dragged. Pasture harrows are available at farm supply stores.

Manure Spreading: When possible, I like to spread the manure from the stalls on empty pastures and paddocks. It's useful for spreading over the thin spots that appear along the fences and across the fields to stop erosion. Spread the manure in thin strips, making rows 20 feet apart in both directions. Spread it thinly and frequently. Let it sit for a few days or weeks, then follow up with chain harrowing. This will fill in the low spots and stop the land from washing away.

You may not be able to spread all the manure your farm creates, especially during the breeding season. We bale the rest of our manure so it can be hauled away easily. If you use straw for bedding, the mushroom farmers may want it. Sometimes the tobacco farmers will pick it up, too. If you do some research, you'll find some type of farmer who can use your manure.

Protecting Trees: Trees are an asset in pastures. They are beautiful and horses appreciate the shade. Unfortunately, they show their appreciation by gnawing on the bark, which will damage or kill the tree. You need to protect the trees from the horses.

We use a simple, inexpensive device that we call a wire basket. It's the type of wire found in dog kennels or hog fences, which is stave wire that's welded at each joint. You need wire nine feet high and 60 inches long to go around a tree trunk 20 inches in diameter. Make a cylinder or tube, lapping the wire over and cutting off the sharp ends.

Take hog rings and fasten it closed from top to bottom around the tree. This makes a safe, sturdy basket. The horse can push it over to eat the grass that grows inside but he can't chew on the tree. He can graze all around the tree and there's no way he can hurt himself. Both the wire and the rings are available at building or farm supply stores.

Wire baskets protect the trees from horses. *(Photo courtesy of Suzie Oldham)*

Chapter 5

Building The Horse Barn

Most horse barns should have a sign posted on the side: "Warning - this building may be hazardous to your horses' health."

The barn poses numerous risks to the health and safety of horses. Horses living in barns develop respiratory diseases from poor ventilation. They slip and fall on the smooth surfaces. They become cast in their stalls. They rear and strike their heads on the beams. Their legs are punctured with forks wielded by careless grooms. Protruding objects cut their flesh. They lose condition from lack of exercise.

As a rule, horses fare better living outside than inside. A barn offers little to the horse in terms of benefits. It's the good grass, fresh air, sunshine and room to gallop that grows fast racehorses. A barn is not the natural home for the horse. Nature intended the horse to live outside. There are only a few occasions when you need a shelter for him. If we keep that in mind, we can design the barn to support our management tactics while minimizing the hazards to the health and safety of the equine occupants.

A barn is necessary for our modern practices which impose artificial schedules and regimens upon the horse. We need to manage horses so they breed, conceive, foal, and mature faster than they would in nature. A properly designed barn allows the breeder to manipulate the horse with the least danger to its well-being.

A horse needs a barn in which he can eat a meal in peace without competing with his pasture mates. Four hours a day inside the barn gives the horse time to clean up his grain, lie down and take a nap. One feeding a day inside is a good management tool. If a horse is injured or off his feed, it is more likely to be noticed if he eats one of his meals in the barn every day.

You need a barn to put your broodmares inside under lights before they are bred. Mares under lights will spend more time in the barn than any other horse. They must be kept out of drafts and their turnout time is limited to the hours of strong daylight.

Manage your broodmares properly and you'll need a foaling stall in your barn. In January, mares should foal in a warm stall and their newborn foals may lie under a heat lamp in the severest cold for the first few minutes of life. But the mare and foal will be moved to a regular stall within a few hours and, within a few weeks, they will spend most of their time outside, as nature intended.

You need a barn for yearlings to prepare them for the sales ring or for training. They will need protection from the hot sun and the flies during the day.

Notice that I have not said one of the reasons you need a barn is to keep horses warm in cold weather. Barns should not be warm. In the winter, the barn should be the same temperature inside as it is outside. If it's five below zero outside, it should be five below inside.

Nature has designed the horse to be "arctic-adapted." A horse only needs a barn during extreme weather which stresses him unnecessarily. The horse does not need to escape from the cold but rather needs protection from sub-zero wind chills and from cold, driving rains. In the wild, the horse can retreat behind a hill or to some other sheltered area. He probably can't do that in your pasture. The barn protects the horses from the sub-zero wind chills from which he cannot escape, not from the cold itself.

Coddling a horse by blanketing and keeping him in an unnaturally warm environment is unnecessary and risks his respiratory health. In a natural environment, the horse grows a thick haircoat and has the good sense to protect himself from the bitter winds. Horses like cold weather. They come out bucking and playing and feeling good. They enjoy it. By designing the barn to approximate natural conditions, we can maintain healthy horses.

While a well-designed barn is not warmer inside during the winter, it is cooler inside than outside during hot weather. To a horse, the most stressful season is summer. A well-designed barn will be five to 10 degrees cooler inside than outside during the summer, making it easier to manage and maintain healthy horses. Heat takes a far greater toll on the health of the horse than cold. Constantly breaking out in a sweat, unable to cool off, the horse experiences much stress in the summer. Insects add to the stress; the continual stomping and shaking wears horses down and causes them to lose condition. Coming into the barn offers welcome relief against the heat and pestilence of summer.

Site Selection, Grade and Drainage: The first step in building a barn is selecting a site which offers adequate drainage. During wet seasons, water must run away from the barn and drain into the surrounding fields. The barn floor should be a minimum of 18 inches above the surrounding grade. Building the barn at least 18 inches higher than the surrounding land and sloping the site away from the barn prevents it from being flooded during heavy rains. The elevation makes it possible to design a drainage plan to quickly move water away from the barn during rain storms. Try to find a naturally high site. A lower site will need more fill to gain the needed height. It's a lot less expensive to build on naturally high ground rather than fill, but this is not always possible.

I do not believe in having rain gutters on my barns. Gutters require downspouts which are dangerous around horses and require considerable attention to keep clean. The rain should run directly off the roof, falling onto gravel or low-growing bushes directly below the edge of the roof. Any water that cannot be absorbed quickly as it flows off the roof onto the gravel or bushes must be made to flow away from the barn. Both shrubs and gravel will catch the rain, but I prefer gravel. Shrubs can interfere with opening and closing the exterior stall doors.

Good drainage requires good engineering. An accurate topographical map is essential to help determine the optimum location for the barn. Involve a good engineer to design the drainage system. It's cheaper to prevent a runoff problem than to cure an existing one.

Floors: While it is important to construct the barn in such a way that it will not be flooded during heavy rains, it is equally important that the floor and the base of the barn be fashioned in such a way to allow water and urine to drain through it. This is accomplished by building a base with 18 inches of coarse, #2 rock, topped with six inches of #6 rock.

As the barn nears completion, this rock will be covered with three inches of coarse asphalt. This allows urine from the stalls to drain through the asphalt, down into the rock and out into the surrounding ground. This is a hot mix asphalt, raked, tamped and laid by hand to remain porous. The mixture is the same for the stalls and for the aisles. The asphalt is laid level, not pitched. Don't let them pack it tight - it won't drain and it will be slippery. Coarsely laid asphalt drains well and, properly installed, will last for many years. This recipe and method of pouring asphalt is so widely used in Kentucky that it is called "stall-mix" here.

Run the asphalt down the aisle and out the door. Lay a wide apron of asphalt 12 to 14 feet out each end of the barn so the horses always walk on the stall-mix asphalt rather than a road-mix, which is slippery. With daily sweeping, asphalt gives a neat appearance and a safe footing on which to show a horse to a prospective buyer.

As time goes by, the asphalt becomes clogged with manure and chaff, slowing the rate of drainage. Stall-mixed asphalt must be pressure-cleaned each year with a steam machine to clean the pores and restore the drainage.

Construction Materials: I favor concrete block over all other construction materials for barns. It is one of the strongest materials available, while requiring the least amount of maintenance. Concrete block is inexpensive and many things can be done to make it attractive. You can paint it, stucco it and put stone around the outside. It even comes in different colors and textures. Concrete block is porous and does not sweat in the summer. I have found it to be the cheapest and best material in the long run.

Poured concrete, on the other hand, is a poor choice for barn construction. Unlike concrete block, it is not porous. It will be damp and will sweat in the summer.

Concrete block is the best material for the exterior of the barn. Wood exterior walls are good-looking, but they are a burden to maintain. Wood must be painted or stained regularly to stay attractive. The good grade of lumber you need for barn construction is expensive.

The best choice for the frame of the barn is wood. Wood is attractive, available everywhere and permits options in the construction style. A steel super structure is satisfactory, but less versatile than wood. It is a little harder to work with than wood which will increase construction costs but, properly constructed, makes a very strong structure.

Metal is a popular choice for the outside walls of barns because it is inexpensive and easy to maintain. Many companies build "pole barns" for horses. It is not my choice because it looks "cold," it's noisy and it's vulnerable to being damaged and dented. In my experience, these buildings don't last.

Insulation: Insulation and vapor barriers are not needed in the horse barn. The purpose of the barn is to provide shelter from the elements, not a warm environment. A properly designed barn will not allow moisture to condense. If you think you need a vapor barrier, you have not addressed the ventilation requirements adequately.

Ventilation - The Most Critical Design Consideration: Of all the hazards posed by a barn, poor ventilation is the most insidious threat. Horses are sensitive to the ammonia, dust and molds that accumulate in a barn. The result may manifest itself as pneumonia in a foal. Older horses may develop more deceptive problems: allergies, emphysema and various maladies labelled as chronic obstructive pulmonary disease, commonly called COPD. Often, you don't realize the damage is occurring until it's too late.

The tip-off to poor ventilation is the ammonia odor produced by urine-soaked bedding. If you smell ammonia when you walk into a barn, you have entered a "danger zone" for horses. Condensation offers another clue to poor ventilation. Warm, stale air condenses on a cold roof in the winter. Frost on the ceiling or - even worse -

mildew, is a sure sign that the air in that barn is not properly exchanged or ventilated.

To provide adequate ventilation, it is important to incorporate a number of principles into the barn which dictate *Shape, Height* and *Stall Design*. I have included drawings of my barn design at the end of this chapter for reference.

Shape: In both hot and cold weather, air should flow freely through the barn providing ventilation without producing drafts. The proper design cools the barn in summer by taking advantage of natural breezes and closes out the cold winds of winter without making the barn too warm. This is easily accomplished. The barn should consist of two rectangles which intersect at the mid-point forming a "+." On each of the four ends are large, sliding doors. I use doors which are 12 feet wide and 10 feet high. In the winter, the doors can be closed on the side from which the cold winds are blowing while leaving the other three doors open for ventilation. In the summer, the open doors on all four sides capture breezes from every direction.

Height Creates Ventilation: A building with a tall pitched roof is not only attractive, it is the best design. A *monitor* roof is the best design for ventilation. The monitor roof has two shed rooflines. A gabled roof, placed on top of the two shed rooflines, forms the peak. Barn walls should be 14 feet high at the eaves. The shed roof rises from the walls at a 6/12 pitch. A vertical section containing 20-inch-high ventilating louvres is placed on top of the two shed roof sections. On top of the louvres is a gabled roof which rises at an 8/12 pitch. From the barn floor to the peak of the gabled roof is 25 feet. In both warm and cold weather, fresh air is drawn into the barn through the open doors, forcing the warm, humid air upward and out through the louvred ridge vents. In warm weather, this process produces cool temperatures in the barn. In cold weather, it produces the air movement necessary to rid the barn of stale, ammonia-saturated air without creating drafts. Remember what I said earlier. In winter, the barn's inside temperature should match the outside temperature. Horses do not mind cold temperatures but they cannot tolerate drafts or high ammonia levels in the air. Horses have a low tolerance for heat in the summer. The barn design I have described solves these problems.

High ceilings provide fresh air without drafts and cool temperatures in summer. Note that there is no hay stored above the stalls.
(Photo courtesy of Suzie Oldham)

One word of caution. All that room above the stalls looks like a good space for hay storage. It is not. Any hay stored above the stalls will restrict the air movement and defeat the purpose of the design I have described. Hay and straw should never be stored in the barn for another reason. Bales of hay produce dust, molds and chaff which horses breathe into their lungs, resulting in respiratory problems.

Aisles and Stall Placement: Stalls are placed along the exterior walls of the two rectangles which form the "+." This creates aisles down the center of both rectangles which intersect at the middle of the barn. The aisles serve as ducts to circulate the air through the barn. At the ends of the aisles are large sliding doors. As the air moves down the aisles, additional fresh air is drawn into the barn through the exterior screen doors in each stall. Never build a barn with a double row of stalls back-to-back. It is nearly impossible to provide adequate ventilation with such an arrangement.

Make your aisles at least 14 feet wide. This width allows enough room for mares and foals. In addition, the staff can muck the stalls and drive tractors through the barn without tearing the doors off. If you are going to ride yearlings in the barn, you will need extra width, a total of 16 feet. I've seen aisles as wide as 20 feet, but this is not necessary.

Stall Design: Each stall has two doors. The aisle door is five feet wide and centered on the stall. It is made of heavy steel mesh screen which allows the free passage of air. A second door is placed in the *exterior* wall directly opposite of the aisle door. Although I call it a door, it may more properly be described as a window, since it is never used to lead horses through except in an emergency. Its purpose is to provide additional ventilation. The outside door frame is eight feet high and four feet wide and rests on one row of concrete block, bringing the top level with the nine-foot stall wall. Encased in the frame, is a steel mesh screen about four feet high, which allows air to blow through the stall. Think of it as the lower half of a Dutch door, which also lets horses put their heads out and view their surroundings. This screen is not a gate and is only removed as an emergency exit. On the outside wall of each stall is a hinged shutter, which is the exterior door. This shutter can be closed to cover the wire mesh door during driving rains or against icy winds.

All door openings are aligned opposite each other on both sides of the aisle. It should be possible for you to stand outside the barn, look into a stall and see across the aisle and through the opposite stall to the outdoors on the other side of the barn.

Stall Size: The proper size for a stall depends on what kind of horse will be using it. The stalls must be large enough so the horse can move away from any drafts that may result from the air moving through the door openings. For yearlings and mares with foals, 12 feet by 14 feet is a good size. If you need more stalls but lack extra space, barren and maiden mare stalls can be made smaller. For these mares that spend a lot of time under the lights, 10 feet x 12 feet is adequate, if not optimum. Foaling stalls need to be large, about 14 by 16 feet. Only foaling stalls have ceilings. Stallions need a stall that is 16 feet by 16 feet. Some of the older farms have stallion stalls as large as 20 feet by 20 feet, but you don't need them that big.

Looking through to the other side shows how the air can move freely through this barn. The exterior door of the stall opens to allow air movement and shuts to prevent drafts.

(Photo courtesy of Suzie Oldham)

Foaling Stalls: The foaling stall has several unique features. It's designed for one event - foaling. It should be constructed of a material that is easy to clean, such as tile, brick or concrete block. The sides of the stall should be padded with smooth-finished tarps or another material that can be cleaned easily. Place the foaling stall next to the watch room, where an attendant can observe the mare and where there is access to hot water and sinks.

To maintain warmth, the stall should have a ceiling with places to attach two heat lamps. Make the ceiling removable, since it is not needed in warm weather. We built a foaling stall ceiling from *Plexiglass*™, which lets light in and can be taken down every spring.

A foaling stall should be equipped with an H-iron to support a block and tackle for a sling. This is used if it is necessary to help the mare to her feet. The H-iron and block and tackle are the same equipment that is used to pull the motor out of a car, so they will not be hard to find. A stall with a sling is also useful if you have a crippled horse. The sling is a worthwhile investment - it may save a mare's life.

Walls: Nine feet is a good height for the walls between adjacent stalls. You don't want to shut out all the light by building the side walls 14 feet high. A five-foot wall with iron grills up to nine or 10 feet is a good alternative to solid walls since some horses are more comfortable if they can see other horses.

Stall walls can be made of oak or concrete block. Pine and other soft woods are not satisfactory for horses because they break and splinter easily. Concrete block is the best choice because horses cannot crib or chew on it. It can be lined with wood or rubber for a horse that kicks.

One of the dangers to a horse kept in the barn is that of becoming cast when it rolls up against the wall and is unable to rise. A cast horse usually panics and may injure himself trying to get to his feet. You can help to eliminate this problem by bolting horizontal ribs or footholds to the stall walls. These footholds are made of hardwood, 1 inch thick by 4 inches wide and beveled for safety. When the horse rolls toward the wall, he can push off the rib with his feet. He either rolls himself over again or pushes himself away from the wall far enough to get up. A second solution is to slant the walls out 12 inches from the floor to about four feet up the sides. Slanting the wall out gives the horse some room for his legs, allowing him to roll on his side a little bit and to put his feet against the wall and push off. The horse is not trapped on his back with his legs straight up in the air. This slanted wall is more expensive to build, but is better for stallions.

The wall of this stallion stall is slanted and ribbed.
(Photo courtesy of Suzie Oldham)

Crossties: According to tradition or to habit, Thoroughbreds are generally not crosstied. Instead, each stall should have a ring mounted on the wall, about five feet high, for tying the horse.

Standardbreds, on the other hand, are normally crosstied for grooming, farrier work, etc. A Standardbred barn needs two rings in each stall for crossties and crossties in a grooming area or in the aisle.

Stall Hardware and Latches: Aisle doors should slide, not swing. Sliding doors need a track at the top of the stall. Buy a good quality track, such as a tube track. A stop is needed to keep the door from sliding off the end of track. The best stop is an iron "L" set into the floor. Don't depend on the door stops that the factory supplies with the track because they always fatigue and break after a few years. Quality materials and proper construction of stall doors will be an economy in the long run.

The frames around the door should have rounded edges. If the stall is constructed of concrete block, the door frame should be made of bull-nose block. A wooden door frame must be beveled so it resembles a fence post. There must be no sharp edges or protrusions that can injure a horse.

Stall door latches are a small item that is frequently overlooked, often with disastrous consequences. Safe stall latches have no protrusions. Whether they are spring loaded or hand held, the safe latch cannot be inadvertently left in a position that sticks out and can catch the horse. A safe latch must be easy to close. You will be holding a horse with one hand. You need a latch that opens and closes quickly, easily and securely without diverting your attention from the horse.

A simple design is best. I recall a rather sophisticated latch that operated from a foot-pedal at the bottom of the door. The problem was that it would clog with straw or dirt and not always work, usually jamming just when a person needed to open or close the stall door quickly. A safe latch works reliably without requiring frequent repairs or adjustments.

Safe examples include a spring-loaded latch mounted above the door and a simple rod on a chain inserted into a hole next to the door frame that blocks the stall door from sliding open. When rod is removed, the door may open and the rod dangles harmlessly from its chain. Safe, effective and it has no moving parts.

To evaluate stall latches, ask yourself, when I take my hand off the latch, what happens? Unsafe latches have protrusions, such as a deadbolt, that can - and surely will - snag a horse and cause serious injury. At the very least, this type of injury leaves an ugly scar, a permanent testimony to poor management. In the worst case, a horse's career on the racetrack is ended by the wrong type of latch on the stall door.

Most hardware and building supply stores do not stock latches that are safe for horse barns. Tack shops in some areas carry good latches, but many do not. It may be necessary to have your latches custom-made. Study the photographs of safe latches and have a welder or metalworker make them for you.

This latch is spring-loaded. Attached to the top of the stall door, it is always out of the way of the horse.   *(RLM photo)*

The latch releases with a tug on the chain, allowing it to pass under the stop and letting the door slide open.   *(RLM photo)*

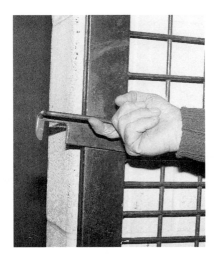

**I simply lift this latch to
hook it over the catch
beside the door.**

(Photo courtesy of Suzie Oldham)

**This latch hangs down
harmlessly when the stall is
unoccupied.**

(Photo courtesy of Suzie Oldham)

**This latch is a simple rod
and pin.** *(RLM photo)*

**Here, the rod and pin are in
the closed position.**

(RLM photo)

Aisle doors are made of heavy screen or mesh. This stall door has a good quality tube track, a safe latch and an "L" stop set into the floor.

(Photo courtesy of Suzie Oldham)

Bull-nosed block used in the stall entrance prevents injuries when leading the horse in and out. Note the wooden block bolted to the concrete which also stops the door. *(Photo courtesy of Suzie Oldham)*

Horses feel less confined if they can put their heads out over a Dutch door. *(Photo courtesy of Z)*

Washracks: A washrack or washstall must provide hot and cold water and a safe place for bathing horses. Construct the washstall with a concrete floor and put a non-slip surface over the concrete to prevent accidents. Do not use asphalt floors in your washstalls. Stall-mixed asphalt does not drain well enough to remove the large amount of waste water. The water would accumulate underneath an asphalt floor and provide a breeding ground for bacteria.

Line the walls with a padded surface to protect a horse that throws his head. We use a rubber-based paint on the floors and walls of our washstalls. Four coats of this rubber-based paint make a cushioned, non-slip surface 1/2 inch thick. Painted over the concrete and the block walls, it makes a safe surface and lasts for three years.

The washstall needs a drain with a catch basin to handle the waste water and debris. The drain leads to a dry well. The catch basin, like a grease trap, collects the hair, mud and manure. It allows you to clean the debris out and avoid plugging the drain.

Washstalls or washracks can also be located outside the barn. If your washrack is outside, put down a base of gravel with stone chips on top for drainage. Drain tile can be put under a wash rack that gets a lot of use. Don't let the run-off go into a paddock.

Right-Angle Turns: One of my favorite devices for training horses to enter a washrack or loading chute is a right-angle turn leading up to it. Young horses that are accustomed to making the right-angle turn to the washrack will approach the loading ramp and readily enter a horse van. Training horses to load using the right-angle turn saves hours of time. The usual coaxing and pushing is eliminated.

The key to this training is the approach to the washrack. Construct a fence or chute to form a 90-degree angle leading up to it. Or use an existing paddock fence as one arm of the angle. The chute must make the horse turn 90 degrees before reaching the washrack. The object is to show the horse nothing but a fence as he approaches. It works because the horse relies so much on his vision for self-preservation. Give him nothing scary to look at and he is apt to do as you wish.

Lead the horse into the chute quietly and confidently. You and the horse must turn right (or left) and as you do, the horse finds himself facing the washrack. This is a natural, no-stress way to train the young horse to approach the washrack and the lesson extends to loading. It makes it easy for the horse to learn about loading in a trailer or van if he's been taught to turn and walk up to the washrack. We get compliments at *Taylor Made* from the van drivers about how well our yearlings load and it's partly because they've already learned the first step of loading from the washrack chute.

The right-angle approach here leads to both the washrack and to the loading ramp. Because the horse sees only the fence and nothing which frightens him, he doesn't "put on the brakes." One 90 degree turn and he's standing at the washrack or the horse van, with no time to anticipate or hesitate.   *(RLM photo)*

Roofs: The best roof is a steel roof. A good quality steel roof is not expensive and goes up quickly, saving money in labor costs. Properly built, a steel roof it will last for years. If you have ever tried to repair a leaky roof, you understand my enthusiasm for a durable, trouble-free steel roof.

The steel roof is supported by 2-inch by 6-inch rafters for a clear span across the stalls. Do not use trusses or pre-fabricated roof rafters. The 2-inch by 6-inch rafters are placed 20 inches apart.

Before putting up the steel, paint the underside of the roofing and rafters. White looks clean and neat and adds a good deal of light to the building. Painting before construction is much simpler than doing it after the roof is up.

My second choice is a shingled roof, made by laying asphalt shingles over plywood decking with a layer of tarpaper over the plywood. This roof looks good from the outside, keeps the heat out and, if well-constructed, lasts many years. However, it will cost more to put up a shingled roof than a steel roof and I believe you will need to replace it before the steel one. Another drawback is the appearance from inside of the barn. The plywood and the nails coming through on the underneath of a shingled roof are not particularly attractive.

Windows: Above the doors at the ends of the barn are large, double-hung windows which can be opened for ventilation. Positioning large windows at the ends of each aisle will let in enough light so electric lights won't be needed during the day.

The windows set into the end doors are also large to let light inside when the doors are closed. The top half of the door should be mostly window. Use grills or wooden frames that give the appearance of several small windows. A large expanse of glass can be hard to see, but the wood frames break it up and make it more visible. These doors will be open whenever horses are passing through the barn. In the fully opened position, they stand against the ends of the building and pose little risk to the horses.

A properly constructed barn that has the outside doors and screens for all the stalls doesn't need a window for each stall. All that's needed is a space 16 inches above each stall under the eaves, sided with fiberglass or *Plexiglass*™ to let in light.

Storage Areas: Design the barns with plenty of storage area. You can't keep a wheelbarrow or stepladder in the aisles. I don't like muck baskets. I hate pitch forks. All of these things must be stored in an enclosed area where no horse will ever come into contact with them. Many a good horse has never seen the racetrack because equipment was stored in the aisle.

Translucent panels under the eaves let light into the stall without the need for extra windows in the barn.

(Photo courtesy of Suzie Oldham)

As you lay out the stalls, set aside three stall spaces per 20-stall barn. The first room stores a week's supply of grain and mineral blocks. This is not a hay storage area. Hay and straw should be brought into the barn daily. Don't store any more hay or straw in the feed room than is required to get through that night. Usually a couple of bales are sufficient until the following morning.

The second room is a warm room for storing medicines that should not freeze, for keeping time-clocks and for providing a convenient place for employees to eat. It needs a refrigerator for medicines and for the employees' lunches and a double sink for veterinary work and for washing up. If the barn is to have a lab, this is the place for it. A bathroom is put at the back of the warm room in each barn, taking advantage of the sinks, hot water and plumbing that serve the warm room.

The warm room in a broodmare barn doubles as a watch room for foaling. Located adjacent to the foaling stall, this warm room has a window into the stall so the foaling man can observe the mare without disturbing her. Use thermal pane glass for the window and cover it with an iron grill on the stall side. (Any windows that can be reached by a horse must be covered for protection.) The room needs only a sink, a chair and a desk. There is no couch, no radio and no TV because this is not a lounge or a place for visiting. Its purpose is to provide a warm place to sit up at night watching mares that are due to foal and a place to write notes or complete charts.

The third room is for tack and equipment. There must be shelves for grooming supplies and hooks for halters and lead shanks, with enough space to hang an extra set that every barn needs. The tack room also stores brooms, rakes, muck buckets and other equipment. You need hooks mounted on the walls so all forks, shovels, brooms and other tools can be hung up. Nothing should be left in the aisle.

Lights & Wiring: In the properly designed barn, stalls will be naturally well lit during the day. However, the night man needs good lighting to check on the horses and the veterinarian will require good light. Each stall needs a 150 to 200 watt lightbulb, centered near the top of one wall. The aisles only need 60 to 100 watts, spaced between stalls so there is one light for every other stall. All stall and aisle lights that horses could contact need a lens guard, which is a heavy glass or wire that covers the light bulb and prevents it from breaking.

Aisle lights are best controlled from a bank of switches close to the main entrance door. You should be able to turn on a block of five or all of the aisle lights upon entering the barn and turn them off as you leave.

A combination light switch and electrical outlet is located between stalls. The electrical outlet is set above the door latch and serves two stalls. Outlets are needed for fans, vacuum cleaners and clippers. A large number of outlets eliminates the problem of running extension cords across the barn. All wiring for lights and outlets must be enclosed in metal conduit. Run the conduit across the ceiling and down behind the posts that frame the stalls. This is safer and adds to the appearance of the barn.

Fire Protection: Few events are as tragic as a barn fire. One of the most crucial aspects of designing a safe barn is the system of safeguards for fire protection.

No matter how careful you are, you cannot rule out the chance that a fire may start. Fires start from tractors, lawnmowers, wiring, smoking, lightning and other acts of God. No amount of precaution will entirely eliminate the possibility, so you must prepare in three ways: (1) Build safety into the barn so a fire is not likely to start and, if a fire does start, it cannot spread quickly. (2) Have the resources on hand to fight a fire until the fire department arrives. Such resources are proper extinguishers for all kinds of fires, including gas and electrical fires. (3) Have a fire plan and conduct regular drills for the employees so no time is wasted in an emergency when every second counts. We have found that instructional meetings conducted by the Fire Department are the best way to impress upon employees the importance of understanding gate numbers, roads and directions and who to call in an emergency.

Fire protection must be built into every barn. Fire safety includes having all wire the correct gauge and enclosed in conduit. Building with a material that is not flammable, such as concrete block, increases the safety factor. Wood, no matter what it is treated with, can never be made totally fire-proof and grows more flammable with age.

Eliminate the causes and practices that start fires. Ban coffee pots and hot plates - coffee pots are the number one source of barn fires. A no-smoking policy in the barn should be strictly enforced. I have found that placing ashtrays at all entrances tells visitors to extinguish their cigars and cigarettes more effectively than any sign. These ashtrays are large, made of heavy plastic and filled with sand. They will not injure a horse, should they be kicked accidently, but they do collect candy and gum wrappers and must be cleaned out regularly. Equip offices and the areas where employees eat lunch with ashtrays.

Tractors, weedeaters and lawnmowers should be maintained in good running condition to eliminate stray sparks. This means that the mufflers and spark arresters are working properly and checked regularly. They should never be started up near barns. All gas cans, paints and solvents must be stored away from the barn.

The hay storage building must be separate from the area where machinery is stored. Hay must be dry before it is put into the building. Spontaneous combustion due to wet hay remains a common cause of barn fires.

Resources for Fighting Fires: Have the proper fire extinguishers accessible and charged. There should be one fire extinguisher at each entrance and one in the office or warm room. Have the extinguishers inspected semi-annually. All employees should be instructed in their use and drilled periodically.

A well-stocked tack room has fire extinguishers within easy reach.

(Photo courtesy of Suzie Oldham)

Planning for Emergencies: Careful planning can mean the difference between a small mishap and a disaster. Put an emergency information card with police, fire department and ambulance numbers next to each telephone. Every employee must know how to contact the fire department and what information to give over the phone. All employees must know how to operate the fire extinguishers and go through fire drills regularly. Memorizing how to evacuate the barn saves precious minutes.

Work with your local fire department and fire marshall in training employees. They are professionals and will offer valuable advice and instruction free of charge. Acquaint them with the entire farm so they are prepared in an emergency. Since most farms have several barns, entrances and gates, you and the fire department must work out a code which explains where the fire trucks need to go. At *Taylor Made Farm*, all gates are coded with a number. By simply saying the number, any employee can tell our fire department exactly where they must go to reach the right barn. After calling the fire department, one person should go out to the gate to wait, in case the fire department needs any further directions.

Water: A reliable supply of water is one of the most important features to build into the barn. If you have ever had your water supply fail on the coldest day of the year and had to haul water for 20 horses, you understand the importance of a reliable source of water. Some type of well-designed, all-weather water hydrant is vital. Look up the coldest day on record - will your hydrant still work? If so, you have the right kind.

The all-weather performance of a hydrant depends on two factors: the hydrant must be supplied by water pipes that are below the frost line, and the hydrant must have a design that allows it to drain completely back into the ground. If your pipes are only three feet deep and the January frost reaches a depth of three and one-half feet, you have a problem. A hydrant must drain completely to be a truly all-weather hydrant. If water remains in the spigot or pipes above ground, it will freeze and you will have to thaw the pipes out or find another source of water.

In addition to being frost-proof, a water hydrant must be safe for use around horses. It should be recessed into the wall, with no pipes sticking out or sharp edges. A Murdock™ hydrant is popular in Kentucky. It is safe, drains well and doesn't freeze.

Each barn needs only one hydrant, but the installation must be planned in advance. A large barn needs a warming room with sinks and a bathroom. A good place for the hydrant is next to the warming room, taking advantage of the plumbing needed for the sinks and the bathroom. Careful planning reduces the length of water and sewer lines required. The drains for the sinks and hydrant should lead into a dry well, which drains outside the barn by way of a PVC pipe. It's not necessary to run the sink and hydrant drains into the sewer or your septic system.

There are two ways to supply water to the stalls - in buckets or with automatic waterers. Any watering system for a horse must be easy to clean. Hay and grain will collect in buckets and waterers, especially from horses that dunk hay or rinse their mouths in their water supply. The water quickly becomes fouled, so there must be a simple way to clean any watering system.

If you use plastic buckets, be sure they are the right kind. The newer plastic buckets are extremely durable and easy to clean because they have a hard, smooth finish. They can be purchased in several sizes and in colors to match your stable colors. The black buckets that are made of heavy, thick rubber are not as satisfactory. The rubber scratches and frays, making them difficult to clean and disinfect.

Buy the right size bucket for the horse. Mares and foals need a five gallon bucket, while yearlings only need 3 1/2 gallons. Mount the snaps about four feet high so the bottom of the bucket is three feet from the floor.

Buckets will increase your labor costs. They must be filled and checked several times a day and, in winter, the ice must be removed. The pieces of ice are as sharp as glass. They must be skimmed out of the buckets, taken outside and discarded a distance from the barn where no one can slip on them.

The advantage to supplying water with buckets is that it allows you to monitor how much water the horse drinks. Going off feed and not drinking water is often the first sign that a horse is not feeling well. If you have a large enough staff for the labor that buckets require, it is a good way to provide water.

The second - and by far the most convenient - way to provide water is the automatic waterer with a heater. Properly wired and installed, automatic waterers provide fresh water reliably in all temperatures. A good automatic waterer has rounded edges and is sturdy enough to withstand some horseplay without breaking. It should have a gallon cup for drinking and an aluminum tray that can be removed for cleaning.

The disadvantage of the automatic waterer is that you cannot tell how much the horse is drinking or if he's even drinking at all unless you see him use the waterer. But a horse on pasture drinks water without supervision. If you are careful to watch your horses, making sure that they are using the automatic waterers, it is an excellent system. It is the freshest, cleanest way of providing water to horses.

Feed Tubs: Feed tubs are placed in the front of the stall, in either corner. This allows the horse to be fed easily. Neither the horse nor the employee have to walk to the back of the stall. It's too easy for an employee to leave the stall door open while feeding. The horse may become distracted and opt for the open door rather than the feed. And a few horses are dangerous to walk past at feeding time. It's a better arrangement to have the feeders in the front of the stall.

The feed tubs can be plastic or metal, but I prefer the new plastic tubs because they are safer. They should hang about 3 1/2 to four feet high. I like to mount snaps to hold them to the wall so they can be taken out and cleaned. You can't do that with a stationary feeder or trough. Feed tubs need to be scrubbed regularly to help prevent disease.

Hay is fed in the back of the stall, in a corner that is swept clean of any dust, dirt or chaff. The reason for this is that the horse will probably defecate as he eats his hay, facing the rear of the stall. The manure is deposited toward the front of the stall, where the night man or groom can simply pick up the manure and put it under the waterer where it won't be trampled into clean bedding. This keeps the manure away from the horse's food. In the morning, the stall can be cleaned quickly. Labor and clean bedding are conserved.

Hay racks aren't needed in the stalls. Sweep out a back corner and place the hay on a clean flake of straw. *(RLM photo)*

Feeding hay off the floor requires good stable management. The area must be swept out daily and it is a good practice to put a clean, unshaken flake of straw where the horse will eat. Hay is piled on top of the straw flake, which catches the leaves and lets the dust and fine particles filter through. When the stall is cleaned, this flake is used for bedding. The area is swept again and a fresh flake of straw is put down. This way, the horse always has a clean spot from which to eat.

Hay racks are acceptable if they are safe and well-made. But horses usually pull the most appetizing pieces of hay out of the rack. The hay falls onto the floor and the horse eats off the floor anyway. The area underneath the rack, too, must be swept daily. The hay rack does not save labor and the routine of sweeping a clean spot to feed hay is good management.

Exercise Pavilions: Every horse farm needs an exercise pavilion, indoor arena or round pen that allows you to turn out every horse every day, regardless of the weather. In cold or rainy weather, it's a good place to turn out mares and newborn foals and yearlings that, due to injury, must be restricted from galloping the length of a pasture or paddock. Horses off the racetrack can often be turned out in an exercise pavilion with less risk of being injured than if they were turned outside. Stallions, which are often neglected as far as exercise, benefit greatly from daily turn-out. The most useful facility for all these purposes is the round pen, described in the chapter, *Yearling Management*.

A proper exercise pavilion is a minimum of 50 feet wide, with 60 feet being an optimum size. The sides must be solid from the ground to at least eight feet high, with no gaps in the boards to catch a hoof. The roof is the most expensive part of the construction of a round pen or an exercise pavilion. I have built them several ways and have found that trusses with a steel roof on top make the best roof for the least money. While it is less expensive to build a round pen or lunging ring without a roof, it won't be of much use in wet weather when you need it the most.

Walkways: Walkways between barns are necessary to ensure good, safe footing year-round. A muddy, unkempt "cowpath" not only looks bad, but it is dangerous in wet weather. Horses must be able to walk safely from the fields into the barn without risking a fall when freezing rain glazes the landscape.

There are several materials that make good walkways, such as stone chips, tanbark or wood chips and crushed brick. These materials drain well and offer non-slip footing in any weather. My number one choice is stone chips covered with wood chips or tanbark. Tanbark and wood chips are softer and more comfortable for barefoot horses than the other materials. Using the two materials together gives both good cushion and good drainage. Water runs through the wood and down through the stone chips. In freezing weather, the wood chips or tanbark will shift underfoot, breaking up the ice.

Brick chips or brick dust make an attractive walkway, adding color and character. It is a safe material for a horse to walk on and it lasts for many years. It's not slippery, even in the winter. Brick naturally has some salt in it that helps to thaw the ice. The ice will just break up under the horses' hooves. The problem is that it's drying to the feet in the summer. The drying effect that brick chips have on the horses' feet offsets its good looks, so brick is my second choice.

Crushed limestone or stone chips, sometimes called "screenings," is an inexpensive and non-slip material. The advantages to stone chips are that it can be raked for a neat appearance and its low cost allows you to replenish it periodically. But it is not satisfactory when used by itself because it loses quality quickly and gets "muddy", producing a kind of gray water that splashes everywhere. Like brick, it dries the horses' hooves. I always add wood chips or tanbark for the top layer, rather than use stone chips by itself.

Brick chips make a handsome walkway.

(Photo courtesy of Suzie Oldham)

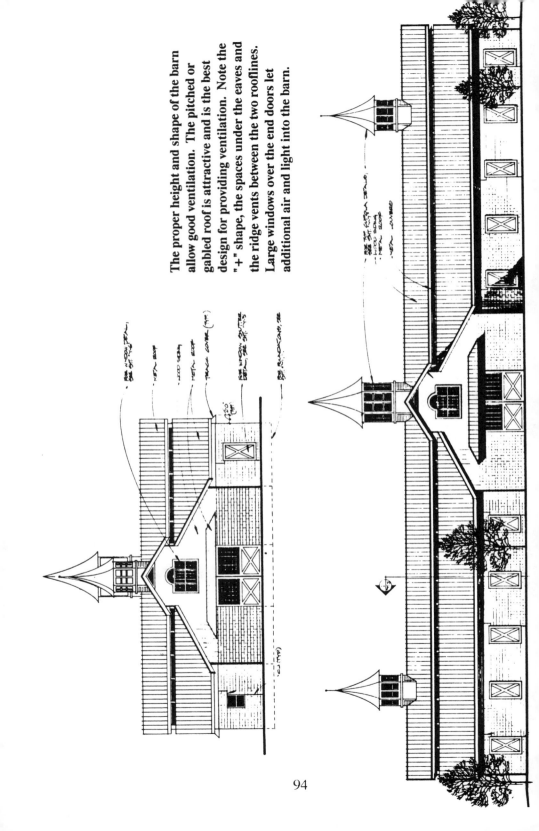

The proper height and shape of the barn allow good ventilation. The pitched or gabled roof is attractive and is the best design for providing ventilation. Note the "+" shape, the spaces under the eaves and the ridge vents between the two rooflines. Large windows over the end doors let additional air and light into the barn.

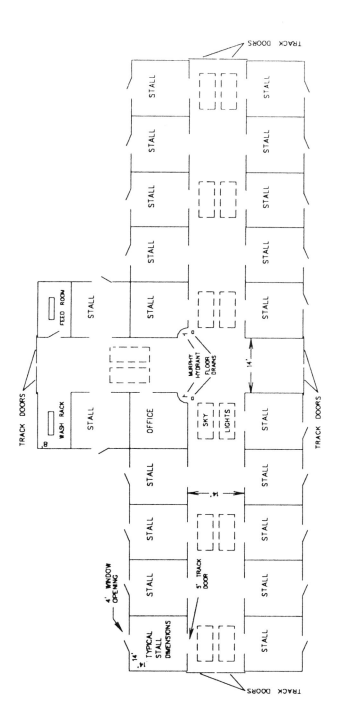

This floor plan shows the relationship of the stalls to the aisles and to the outside that allows ventilation.

Part II

Finding and Breeding
Good Horses

Chapter 6

Choosing Good Advisors

Every successful business operates on inside information and nowhere is this more true than in the horse business. The outsider who attempts to work his way through the maze of relationships, deals, favors and tips is at a disadvantage. You need advice from professionals who have been actively involved in the business for years. Without access to this kind of expertise, it is impossible to make the subtle distinctions and choices necessary for survival. Good advisors steer you toward other quality people and toward quality horses.

But there is a right way and a wrong way to use advisors. Conventional wisdom says, hire a good advisor, then confide to him your goals and the amount of money you are willing to risk. Armed with this knowledge and your checkbook, the advisor will purchase the horses he thinks you need. After purchase, hired managers and other professionals look after them as they see fit. Periodically, you are apprised of the progress of your horse business. The need to upgrade your stock will almost always be suggested. Your advisors and hired professionals relieve you of any need to become involved in the day-to-day affairs of your horse business.

Read the above paragraph again replacing the word "horse" with the name of the product or service which earned you the money to begin investing in horses in the first place. If you follow this advice in any other business, you will be plucked clean in a short time. The same is true in the horse business.

One of your first goals in the horse business must be to cultivate a wide circle of contacts you can turn to for information and advice. But a successful owner does not give anyone carte blanche with his checkbook. He solicits advice and opinions from many experts and the advice and opinions he receives will oftentimes conflict. Based on what he learns and what his instincts tell him, the owner makes all crucial decisions for his business. Building on strategies that were successful and discarding those that were not, he continues to educate himself and surrounds himself with competent people. In all instances, however, he reserves for himself the final decisions which must be made on behalf of the business.

Equally foolhardy is the novice who believes he needs no advice or input from any professional. I'm always amazed at people who ordinarily require blueprints, plans, projections, prospectuses and every conceivable piece of information before investing $300,000 in any other venture, but who go out and spend the same amount on a horse without knowing anything about it. Invest in the horse business using the same logic you use in your other business transactions.

Why You Need Help: The benefit of an advisor can be illustrated with an example. Perhaps you are considering a nice, well-bred broodmare. She has had some success at the track and a close relative was a successful racehorse. This mare's price is suspiciously low because she has yet to produce a runner. Her only two foals did nothing to build her reputation or enhance her value. One broke down at the track and the second had wind problems - neither trained well enough to start a race. A good advisor may discover the whole story about this mare. The *whole* story is that the mare's first offspring broke down because one foot was poorly conformed - a defect that appears in the foal's sire line. The second had pneumonia as a foal. He spent a month laying down and his wind never fully recovered. The mare's bloodlines are good, she is not to blame for her first two foals. Her best foal is yet to come. This is powerful information.

Consult your advisors, consider their opinions but make your own decisions on investing in horses. You will be respected by honest horsemen who know that no one spends money more carefully than the guy who made it.

Getting Help: There are a variety of sources for good advice and the best advisor varies with each situation. The expert you need may be a bloodstock agent, an experienced fellow breeder, a farm owner or manager, a trainer, a veterinarian or one of a variety of specialty advisors. No one person is an expert in all phases of the racehorse business.

Bloodstock Agents: For assistance with buying horses, a bloodstock agent is often your best bet. A bloodstock agent specializes in buying and selling horses. A good bloodstock agent offers a variety of services, including pedigree and performance research, bidding for you at the sales and finding "hot" stallion seasons and shares. Some prep yearlings and board and foal broodmares. Others specialize in horses that are on the track. Whatever you may need, from appraisals to vanning to lay-ups, a bloodstock agent will know someone who provides that service.

Because there is no license or certification required to be a bloodstock agent, choosing a good one is not as simple as finding a CPA or a doctor. You have only his reputation and past performance to go on. To protect yourself against dishonest or incompetent practitioners, do some research before choosing one.

A good bloodstock agent will give you a list of his current and past clients. You may draw some conclusions from the names on the list, but follow up and contact these people. Ask them how the agent performs. Does he have good information and good contacts? Does he listen to his clients and keep them informed? Is he honest? Would they use him again?

A bloodstock agent may keep statistics on how his recommendations have performed as investments for other clients. Ask for this type of information and study it. If the figures seem too good to be true, they probably are. The honest bloodstock agent's record can be believed and verified.

After you have compiled a list of agents with good references, meet with each of them. Prepare a list of questions to ask and don't be afraid you'll look foolish! You'll be relying on this person to help you build your business and fulfill your dreams. Make sure you are compatible with each other, and comfortable and confident with his abilities.

In the horse business, as in any other, you must pay for good advice. A bloodstock agent is usually compensated through a commission arrangement. If the bloodstock agent gives you specific advice about which horses to buy - and which ones to avoid - he is entitled to a commission on each of your purchases. As a rule, a bloodstock agent charges about 5% for finding a horse for you. If he finds a mare and you pay $30,000 for her, you will pay him a $1,500 commission.

Your survival in this business may not depend upon how many good horses your bloodstock agent steers in your direction. Rather, your survival will more likely depend upon buying as few poor horses as possible. The best advice your bloodstock agent may ever give you is to keep your checkbook in your pocket. When your bloodstock agent gives you this advice, he does so at his own financial disinterest if his only compensation is a commission on your purchases. Any arrangement based solely on commission may tempt some agents to find you a horse to buy, even if it's not the best deal. Structure your relationship with your bloodstock agent so he is compensated whether you buy something or not. Give him an incentive to encourage you not to buy when the situation so dictates. This puts both of you on the same team.

It is not necessary to employ one bloodstock agent exclusively. It can be to your advantage to employ a number of agents. The value of a second opinion is obvious. Less obvious, but equally important, is maintaining independence from any single advisor. Developing a healthy competition among several agents for your business may result in a larger selection of good prospects. Don't entrust only one individual with all your buying decisions, don't tell anyone how much you're willing to spend, and don't feel that any advisor has the right to know anything about your business other than what you're willing to divulge.

Trainers: When you are looking for horses to race, a trainer is an excellent choice as an advisor. A trainer's advice is most useful when buying horses that are in training or already racing or when evaluating yearlings. A trainer survives by having an eye for a racehorse - he cannot afford fashions or market trends. A trainer has a keen appreciation for racehorses that pay the bills. For the broodmare buyer, a trainer will often know who has young race mares for sale at the track.

If the trainer you choose will also be training the horse, you have another advantage. He may have more enthusiasm for a horse he participated in selecting. He will be less apt to assign any poor performance from the animal to its conformation or lineage, since he would be condemning his own judgment.

The big advantage that a trainer has is first-hand knowledge of particular horses on the racetrack. There are few secrets on the backstretch. If certain horses don't want to run, break down easily or can't be trained, a trainer will know it. He may know that the horse's family shows similar defects. This is particularly useful information when considering racing stock by stallions whose get are just beginning to hit the racetrack. Trainers will be the first to know which young stallions are producing runners and which ones are not.

The risk in using a trainer as an advisor is the risk you always run when asking someone you don't know very well, "What do you have that I should buy?" Training racehorses is a tough business; a trainer in financial straits might see you as the answer to his prayers. And, racing luck being what it is, the racetrack is the riskiest place to invest and offers the least accountability.

Read the trade magazines to find the successful trainers in your area. Check the statistics - they are available on every aspect of a trainer's performance. Read them thoroughly and a picture will emerge of the trainer's strengths and weaknesses. Visit the track in the morning - whose operation looks professional and deserving of your money? Talk to the top trainers. If you can afford them, wonderful. If not, they may have apprentices or know young, reputable trainers. Interview your candidates and check with their owners to see how each performs for them. Allow time to thoroughly research a trainer's reputation. There are many competent, honest people training horses and they are the ones who deserve your business.

Like a bloodstock agent, a trainer is entitled to a commission or other compensation for the advice he gives. You may ask your trainer to accompany you to a sale and help you select horses to buy. You can't expect the man to take the time off, pay his own expenses and give you his advice without compensation for his services. A few dishonest trainers may even make an agreement behind your back with the sellers. You don't get something for nothing very often in this business.

A better arrangement is to discuss your plans with the trainer, offer to pay his travel expenses and ask him if he would agree to a lower commission on your purchases, perhaps 2 1/2% of each horse. He may agree to these terms or he may negotiate a different fee arrangement. Either way, he'll be on your side when you get to the sale.

Fellow Owners: Seminars for new owners, such as those sponsored by the Thoroughbred Owners and Breeders Association (TOBA) and the various state associations, are worth attending. The seminar organizers usually arrange for a number of successful breeders and trainers to meet with new owners. You will meet people who share your interests and others who are attempting to establish themselves in the business just as you are. A friendship can lead to shared knowledge and shared investments. The contacts you make at these meetings can lead you to qualified people of every profession. A fellow owner may recommend a good advisor or bloodstock agent who has served him well. You may even benefit from a fellow owner's mistakes, if that person is brave enough to share them with you.

You might be lucky enough to form a friendship with a leading breeder of racehorses. This industry has breeders who have been in the business all their lives. Some are independently wealthy people who have no restrictions on their buying and breeding decisions, a freedom for experimentation unavailable to most. If you are fortunate enough to have such a person to consult, consider his or her advice carefully. These men and women know as much about horses as anyone alive.

Be cautious about taking advice from the inexperienced breeder and steer clear of the guy who "knows it all." Someone who has only been in the business a few years longer than you is still making mistakes and learning things the hard way. Or worse, he has had a modest success which convinces him he knows everything there is to know about racehorses.

Veterinarians: A veterinarian is an integral part of your team of advisors. The advice of a veterinarian is needed when purchasing broodmares. A broodmare is worthless if she is not breeding sound, a condition which is not evident without a veterinary exam. An in-foal mare may seem like a guarantee of breeding soundness - it is not. There is no substitute for the veterinary pre-purchase exam for prospective broodmares or other horses you are interested in buying. Sometimes the seller will provide records of veterinary examinations conducted to facilitate the sale. These records should be verified by a veterinarian on your payroll. After you have purchased your horses, you will need the services and advice of a good veterinarian for the numerous problems that are likely to arise.

Choose a veterinarian the way you would choose a bloodstock agent or trainer - start at the top and see where it leads you. Which veterinarian do your area's top horsemen employ? He or she may accept you as a client. If not, a qualified colleague will be recommended. Veterinary schools will recommend veterinarians in your area. Take this one step further - talk to their Chief of Surgery or Chief Internist about your needs and your concerns. You will be given the names of veterinarians who are well qualified to help you.

Specialty Advisors: Within the racehorse industry are many areas of specialized study that may help predict performance or highlight potential problems. You might employ the services of a veterinarian whose research into the breathing efficiency of racehorses helps you to select a horse. Or, you might choose an expert who has studied and quantified conformation into a formula that may predict future racing ability. A nutritional advisor may point out nutritional deficiencies that led to poor performance and offer solutions to the problem. There are consultants for pedigree research, nicking patterns or research on foreign racehorses. In fact, it is hard to find any aspect of breeding or racing that does not have an expert. The trade magazines list most of the commercial consultants, while veterinary schools can put you in touch with medical researchers.

Obviously, the risks are the same as with any other expert. You should be the beneficiary of the expert's research - not part of it. Recognize the narrowness of the specialist's expertise. While his depth of knowledge of certain aspects of horses may be impressive, you shouldn't rely totally on his advice. Use this expert's knowledge in concert with advice from other sources.

Developing Business Relationships: If you hire the best advisors, be a client of the same calibre. Return phone calls, pay your bills and be on time. If you hire a person of integrity and deal with that person in a straightforward manner, recognizing that his time is worth something and that he has to make a living, you will be treated in kind.

Being straightforward is not the same as being naive. It is possible to encourage dishonest or unethical practices. Never divulge to your advisor how much you will actually spend on a horse. If he is doing the bidding for you, indicate a conservative price range. Only you should know much you are willing to pay and at what point you intend to drop out. Only an extraordinary amount of trust justifies telling an agent or advisor what your top dollar really is. Finally, you must negotiate a dollar limit with that most difficult, impulsive party of all - you. Know your limit and resist the temptation to exceed it in the excitement of the sale.. Treat your horse purchases as business decisions. There will always be good horses and chances to buy them. Wait for the opportunities. We want you in this business for the long run!

Chapter 7

Broodmare Selection

The greatest thrill in the horse business is breeding a horse that goes on to win something of significance. This is something special, and the goal of every breeder. Your chances of achieving this distinction are better if you assemble the best broodmare band possible. Broodmares are the backbone of a breeding operation. You may have an elegant farm, but only your broodmares will make you a reputation for producing quality racehorses.

People in the racehorse breeding business are usually more concerned with the pedigree of the stallion than with the pedigree of the broodmare. This is a mistake. The mare contributes 50% of the gene pool of the foal. If 50% of your gene pool comes from poor racing stock, you are likely to get something other than a good racehorse. A *good* broodmare may have 25% or more of her progeny become stakes winners. But the *average* mare will produce nothing but average or below average racehorses.

Stallions are culled more objectively than broodmares. Generally, only stallions which have won important races are allowed to stand at stud, with a few notable exceptions for those with powerful pedigrees. Despite this rigorous culling process, a stallion which can produce 10% stakes winners from starters is considered by most people to be an outstanding sire. How can it be that an outstanding sire will have a lower percentage of stakes winners than a good broodmare? It's simple. A stallion must service all the mares brought to him, the good ones and the bad ones. Claiborne Farm used to have a saying, "Stallions' reputations are made with other people's mares." And it's true. Bad mares can make even an outstanding sire look bad.

In many ways, trying to breed a fast racehorse is like rolling the dice. There is no guarantee what the result will be. But rolling a winning number is even harder if one of the dice is missing some of its spots. It's not impossible to breed a winning racehorse using below-average mares. It's just a lot harder.

Breeding Goals: The first step toward breeding a racehorse is to have a clear idea of the type of horse you want to breed. Everyone wants to breed a "good" horse but the term "good" is too vague. Ask yourself exactly what it is that you want the horse to do and what qualities it will need to accomplish its purpose. You need a mental picture of the horse you hope to breed. The picture you have formed will dictate both the type of mares and stallions you need.

If you are breeding Thoroughbreds, your goal, of course, is to win races. But at what distance? Do you want to breed a sprinter or a horse that can stay the distance?

I believe the safest goal is to breed for the mile. I say this for three reasons. First, I believe that American racing fans like to see and bet on speed races. In my opinion, the future of Thoroughbred racing in North America rests with shorter, fast races, somewhere between six furlongs and a mile. More and more races and, consequently, more and larger purses will be available to horses that can compete at these distances.

Second, breeding a racehorse remains an inexact science. If you breed for the mile and miss the mark, you still have somewhere to go. If the horse you bred cannot win at the mile, you still have an opportunity to run him at shorter or longer distances. By running him at different distances, you may ultimately find one that suits him. But if you breed for the extreme end of the spectrum and you miss your mark, you have only one direction in which to move. If you don't get the six-furlong sprinter you bred for, you can only move up in distance. If you miss the mark at 1 1/2 miles, the only way to move is down.

Third, I believe that breeding for a specific distance - preferably a mile - is a way of keeping your breeding program on track. It's a way of gauging whether you are succeeding at what you are doing. The Standardbred industry breeds only for the mile. A pacer that can win at only six furlongs is as useless as one that can only win at 1 1/4 miles. Perhaps that is why Standardbred breeders have made so much progress over the past several decades in breeding faster horses. At any rate, if you are breeding for milers and end up with only sprinters, you must examine what you are doing wrong.

As a Standardbred breeder, you must decide if you are looking for a trotter or a pacer and at what age you hope to win races. Standardbred breeders must be even more discerning when selecting broodmares because the speed of the Standardbred is increasing so rapidly. The dramatic improvements in times - at all levels, stakes races to claiming races - have raised the standard for good breeding stock at a dizzying rate. What was a quality mare in the 1980s is probably not a good enough mare to breed profitably in the 1990s. The Standardbred breeder must be constantly poised to cull his broodmare band and upgrade his stock to remain on top of this ascending curve.

And one of the most important decisions for any racehorse breeder is whether to sell or race your foals.

Breeding for the Market: The recipe for success in breeding yearlings with the goal of selling them profitably at the select sales is (1) to breed a horse with a strong pedigree; (2) to limit your breeding program to mares and stallions whose progeny have consistently brought high prices in the past or, alternatively, which you have good reason to believe will bring good prices in the future because of some recent development; (3) to structure your breeding program to produce yearlings of unusually good conformation, especially avoiding defects that the buyers find objectionable; and (4) to breed for early maturation that will result in big, well-developed horses by the summer or fall of their yearling year when buyers look at them.

The saleable youngster is, above all, fashionably bred. His sire is in great demand for having sired a high percentage of stakes winners or the sire is a recently retired racehorse with a great reputation that is still fresh in the minds of the yearling buyers. Breeding to a first or second year sire of note is a good strategy for the market breeder. If the offspring are good-looking, they often bring better prices than the get of a sire with a proven record of stakes winners.

The dam of the saleable yearling is from an important family. Her offspring have a record of selling for high prices. Or the yearling is the first out of a well-bred young mare that inspires optimism in yearling buyers Such a yearling is often the result of a popular nick or combination of bloodlines thought to produce speed. Great expectations surround the saleable youngster because of his illustrious relatives. His value is determined, in part, before he is even born. You could compare this colt to a work of art - he has a certain, intrinsic value simply because he was made by someone famous.

Of course, races are won and records are broken by horses from obscure families. Everyone knows that a good pedigree is not a guarantee of success. But if your mare has no pedigree worthy of note, the buyers won't look at her foals. If you're breeding young horses for the sales ring, you would do well to follow the fashions. You will run out of money before you start your own trend.

Ideally, the mare you select to breed for the sales ring is a nine year old that has produced three stakes winners. But everyone wants this ideal mare - her price will be astronomical. More affordable is the young race mare that is carrying her first foal. This can be a remarkably good mare to produce yearlings for the sales ring. Potential buyers often take a hard look at the first few yearlings from a decently bred young mare. This concept is discussed in detail later in this chapter.

Then, too, there is the issue of conformation. Sales ring conformation is different than racetrack conformation. When breeding for market, you want to select mares with a history of throwing correct foals. In recent years, buyers have become more and more critical of conformation. Seattle Slew toed out. This was not an impediment to winning the Triple Crown. His conformation problem, however, proved to be a major problem in the sales ring. He sold for a bargain $17,500 as a yearling.

One conformational defect that dooms almost any yearling in the sales ring is to be "back at the knee." Buyers want flat, correct knees with no tendency to deviate backwards.

The size of the yearling is another factor to be considered when breeding for the market. Buyers want big yearlings. The size of the yearling can be determined, in part, by breeding strategy. An early breeding will give the foal more time to grow before the sales than will a late breeding. But size is also a genetic factor. Small mares tend to throw small foals. Some mares are genetically programmed to throw smaller foals than others. A mare that has already had several foals has a history that can be researched to determine what type of foal she produces.

It's not that small horses aren't good racing prospects. It's just that the market won't pay much for them. The market breeder must breed his mares early and avoid those mares that throw small or slow-growing foals. When E. P. Taylor tried to sell Northern Dancer as a yearling, nobody wanted him. He was too small. Apparently Mr. Taylor didn't want him either or he wouldn't have put him in the sale. The best thing that ever happened to Mr. Taylor and was getting stuck with this horse that nobody wanted.

Your decision whether to breed yearlings for the sales or to race them yourself may not be an "either/or" proposition. No matter how earnestly you devote yourself to breeding handsome, fashionably bred youngsters, if they are not sold, you will be in the racing business. The fact that your yearlings are not saleable leaves you with only one option: race them and prove their worth. An unsold crop of yearlings must go to the racetrack, otherwise you are breeding very expensive hunter prospects.

You cannot go far wrong if you adopt my goal, which is to breed sound, athletic young horses that are marketable as yearlings and which will become quality racehorses. The ideal is to breed for both, and wherever your breeding interests lie, it is worth bearing in mind.

Breeding for the Racetrack: If your goal is to breed a racehorse to race yourself, your broodmare selection criteria is somewhat different than if you are breeding for market. Federico Tesio, considered by many to be the greatest Thoroughbred breeder of the 20th century, was fond of saying: "The Thoroughbred exists because its selection has depended not on experts, technicians or zoologists but on a piece of wood: The winning post of the Epsom Derby." Tesio never bred his

111

horses for the marketplace. He cared little about what the bloodstock agents at Newmarket thought about the salability of his yearlings. Tesio's goal was to breed good racehorses and he did so with a relatively small band of broodmares, many of which he bought at bargain prices. Except during the war years, he never stood his own stallion. He concentrated his efforts on assembling the best mares possible.

Tesio knew what no one dares to say. If the horse can win, it doesn't matter what he looks like or how unpopular his pedigree. If you breed to race, you have only one criterion and that is to breed horses that win. However, this is a narrow path that is seldom travelled and making this your only goal could produce horses that can't get into any sale. On the other hand, you may have some luck and catch lightning in a bottle.

If you want to breed for the racetrack, I believe that the best strategy is to assemble a band of young mares that have proven racing records. More and more horseman are beginning to believe that the mare's best foal is likely to be among her first five foals. I have seen this be the case many times and I tend to agree with the theory.

Select mares which have demonstrated racing performance. Ideally, the mare has won a few important stakes races or, at the very least, has shown the ability to win at the upper end of the allowance classes. A mare which once showed class but has fallen into the claiming ranks because of a racing injury or bad management may be a bargain choice. On the other hand, steer clear of those mares which could only win in restricted races or which won only against inferior company.

If you are a Thoroughbred breeder, remember what I have previously said about breeding for the mile. The mare you select should have demonstrated winning ability at a distance of about a mile. If she showed versatility and won at several distances, so much the better. On the other hand, think twice about mares that showed winning ability in only sprints or routes.

Finally, do not overlook pedigree when breeding for racing. The mare's pedigree need not be fashionable but it should show depth. By depth, I mean that her pedigree should be sprinkled with a large number of ancestors which demonstrated speed on the racetrack and which produced winners as well. I will explain more about depth of pedigree later in this chapter.

The better the mare performed on the racetrack, the more forgiving you can be about her pedigree. Or, stated another way, the less evidence there is that she was a good racehorse herself, the stronger the pedigree must be.

Conformation is not the issue that it is for the sales ring. If the mare toes out a little or is slightly back in her knees, it may be forgiven if she raced well and stayed sound. You win by a head. Not a pretty head.

Size and the appearance of early maturation are not as important if you intend to race yourself. By the second or third year, most smaller colts and fillies have caught up to their larger stablemates in development. Size is not an index of speed or stamina. There are many more good 15.3 hand racehorses than there are good 17 hand racehorses.

True maturation is another matter, unrelated to size. It is important to have a horse mature in his athletic abilities early in life. The high cost of keeping a horse in training dictates that horses race as two-year-olds. To qualify for the classics, a horse must prove himself in his second year. As a three-year-old, the competition escalates. Three year-olds must take on the world. Those horses that don't come into their own until the third or fourth year are at a disadvantage. The good broodmare for the racehorse breeder throws foals that realize their athletic potential early in life.

The Basis for Selecting Broodmares: Whether you are breeding for the market or for the racetrack, there are six criteria for selecting broodmares: pedigree, production, performance, conformation, age and pocketbook. And, if you are buying a broodmare that is in-foal, add two more: the value of the covering sire and the covering date.

Choosing a broodmare is not a matter of deciding among these criteria but rather that of balancing their strengths and weaknesses. Any broodmare you consider will be a compromise and, to some extent, a gamble. The very top mares that have produced graded stakes winners and which are still producing foals are only available to the truly deep-pocketed. They are generally not for sale until they are quite old. You must weigh the good points of each mare against her shortcomings in pedigree, conformation and age and so forth. The more information you have about the mare, the better able you are to make a decision of whether to invest in her.

Pedigree: A good pedigree in a broodmare shows both performance and depth and these two concepts are closely related. In the ideal world, every name in the pedigree will be occupied by an outstanding racetrack performer which, in turn, became either a sire or dam of other outstanding performers.

In the real world, there are no such perfect pedigrees but it's important to find broodmares with as much depth to their pedigrees as possible. By depth, I mean superior individuals occupying as many places in the pedigree as possible in as many generations back as possible. When you find racing performance from top to bottom and stretching back into a horse's pedigree, you have depth. A shallow pedigree is one which has only a few outstanding performers within the first few generations. I don't know what you call a pedigree with only a few superior performers sprinkled randomly throughout the various generations. Such a mare is likely to produce foals more suitable for English equitation than for racing. Only a truly outstanding race record can excuse a mare from the requirement of a strong pedigree.

In terms of genetic influence, it is more interesting than helpful to research the pedigree of a horse beyond the fourth generation. An isolated ancestor beyond the fourth generation is unlikely to have much effect on the next generation. Then, too, there is the matter of the hanky-panky that went on with the Stud Book back before we had blood typing. Prior to the advent of blood typing, I believe the Stud Book is only about 85% accurate.

I have heard of one prominent breeder who would boast that he "never had a good mare go barren." He owned quite a few mares and each year he would book one of the better ones to a well-known stallion. He would then send whatever mare was in heat to the stallion and he always demanded a "triple." In other words, he would have her bred in the morning, again in the afternoon and a third time the next morning. After each cover, he took the mare home and hauled her back again for the subsequent covers. Of course, it never was the same mare. He would breed three separate mares all on one stud fee. Later, he would select the foal that he wanted to be by this stallion and assign the other two foals to his own stallion which he stood. At least two and probably all three foals were reported inaccurately in the Stud Book. With blood typing, you can't get away with that kind of thing any longer.

Not all inaccuracies in the Stud Book have resulted from dishonesty. Many of them are honest mistakes. I have accidentally bred the wrong mare to the wrong horse. A breeding farm is a busy place at the height of the breeding season. The stallion manager and his staff are in charge of breeding numerous mares each day, most of which they have never seen before. Even today, a stallion will, on occasion, be put to the wrong mare. Every time I had bred the wrong stallion to the wrong mare, I'd wash her out and start over. It might have cost me a stud season, but it had to be corrected. Today's blood typing techniques will catch such mistakes sooner or later. Before blood typing, such mistakes would go undetected.

Production: The best mares are winning daughters of mares that produced other winners. Trace back the pedigree of mares three or four generations. You're looking for mares that have strong families and that means the mare's dam is a strong mare, that her grandam is a strong mare and that her great-granddam is a strong mare. What you are doing here is tracing back the bottom line, or female line, of the pedigree. By strong, I mean you want the mother, grandmother and great-grandmother of your mare all to have been winners and all to have produced other winners. In the real world, you never find the pedigrees to be as strong in production as you would like.

Fertility is another aspect of production to consider. Certain families are not as fertile as others, and some are notorious for producing offspring which cannot reproduce themselves. Check how many foals the second, third and fourth dams produced. If these mares had only two or three foals each, you cannot realistically expect their descendant, the mare you are looking at, to produce more than two or three foals herself.

As you check production records, do your research thoroughly - some families are deeper than they appear. I recall a good race mare whose second and third dams were "blank," having had only one foal each, while the fourth dam was a strong producer. On the basis of this information alone, you might conclude that this mare probably won't be a strong producer. What the record didn't show was that the second and third dams both died after having only one foal. It wasn't their fault that they had no production record. And that, as Paul Harvey says, is the rest of the story.

Performance: Performance is the record which the mare assembled as a racehorse. Ideally, a mare has both performance and pedigree to recommend her. But any filly that wins a graded or other important stakes race has just rewritten her own pedigree. Excellence on the racetrack reflects favorably on all relatives as well as the winning racehorse. A Grade I or II stakes winner will be hard to touch, but there are many other races of varying degrees of prestige for fillies. A filly that trains and races well, and remains sound, is a good prospect for the broodmare buyer. Don't rely totally on black type. Any filly that shows speed over distance and has some good blood behind her is worth considering.

Conformation: Good conformation is important for both sales and racing purposes. A well-made horse is like a wheel with all of its spokes and the rim having equal strength and balance. It just keeps on rolling. A bad spoke will shorten its useful life and cause it to break down. Study conformation. Learn everything you can and keep learning as you go.

A well-made broodmare is the same as any other horse with good conformation in that she has good balance and proportion, good legs, etc. However, she must conform to one additional uncompromising principle: She must be capable of carrying and delivering a foal. Look for well-sprung ribs and ample hindquarters. A rectangular profile is thought to be good broodmare type, as opposed to the horse that fits inside a square.

Have any prospective broodmare examined by a veterinarian who can determine if a young mare is fully developed and if an older mare is breeding sound. External anatomy of the reproductive organs gives an important clue. The vulva of a good broodmare will be vertical and located mainly below the level of the pelvic floor. A broodmare that lacks this correct reproductive anatomy will require special veterinary measures to remain breeding sound.

This well-conformed broodmare passed her straight, correct legs and good balance on to her foals. *(Photo courtesy of Martin Pierce)*

You may see some older mares that aren't very attractive. Some are sway-backed and in others, the pelvis is bony and appears to lack muscle. Such mares should be forgiven if they have already produced several foals which caused them to lose their girlish figures. As long as the foals are correct, these defects don't matter.

A mare that is "pony-fat" is another story. I don't like to see mares with thick, cresty necks and two inches of fat over the ribs. This overly fat condition may indicate a metabolic defect. Even with perfect health, overweight mares have more trouble settling in foal and delivering their foals.

One of the most overlooked items of conformation among broodmare buyers deals with the tendency of some mares to colic during pregnancy. If a mare is predisposed toward colic during pregnancy, this could be the real reason she is being offered for sale. Before buying any broodmare, it is important to determine if she has had a history of colic. Be sure to check for scars which indicate past colic surgery. The scars can be found along the bottom of the abdomen, running toward the udder. Any type of abdominal surgery will leave a similar scar, and some surgeries have no reproductive repercussions. But a mare that has had several feet of intestine removed during colic surgery is more likely to colic again in the future - before, during and after pregnancy - than is a mare with no history of serious colic. Even if she and the foal survive the colic, the veterinary expenses can be prohibitive. It is vitally important to get the medical history behind the scar before you buy this mare. A mare with a record of colic is a risk.

Another item relating to conformation to be investigated is the mare's ability to produce sufficient milk for her foal. You can't tell by looking at a mare how much milk she produces and how good it is. This is part of her history and you should know about it. If a mare has failed to make enough milk in the past, you will need to line up a nursemare before the foal comes. This is another expense, so be sure the mare is worth it.

Age: Age is a complex issue when you are evaluating broodmares. There is a bias against older mares. Some of this is based on hard facts and statistics, some of it stems from the prejudices and wishful thinking that are part of human nature. If you understand the bias, you can turn it to your advantage.

A young mare with a decent pedigree, perhaps one fresh off the racetrack, is often the one that will produce the most saleable yearlings. Many people believe that a mare's best foals are her first five. I tend to agree with this, but the point is that this is what yearling buyers believe. You can make this work in your favor.

Consider the young, unproven mare as a gun with four bullets in the chamber. She has four shots to make it before her true value as a broodmare is known. A fairly well-bred, young mare that was covered by a promising young stallion and produces foals with good conformation, is a producer of truly saleable yearlings. In the minds of the yearling buyers, this is a good cross and anything can happen *because it hasn't been proven that this doesn't work.* This is an important point. Human nature is hopeful and buyers are almost anxious to believe that this mare's yearlings could really make it.

This strategy works for the first four foals out of a young mare. No one will know if she can produce good racehorses until after her fourth foal is raced and the first four will sell easily. The market will even forgive the mare for four "bad" foals. Up until the fifth foal, you could probably sell this mare and get your money back out of her.

Decide whether or not the mare has a shot at producing a stakes winner while she is carrying her fourth foal. This is the time to make your decision to keep her or to sell her. By the time fifth foal arrives, the mare will have three years of offspring with race records. By the fifth foal, everyone will know if she has produced a winner. And if the statistics read "3 starters, 0 winners," everyone will know that this mare hasn't hit the mark. Make this decision before the rest of the world makes it for you.

A somewhat older mare that has had several nice foals but none truly outstanding, is considered a mare "in limbo." While such a mare hasn't produced a stakes winner yet, she has several more years to hit the mark. This mare is a gamble. To the market buyer, she is less likely to produce a top foal than is a young, unproven mare. The selling price of this slightly older mare's foals will reflect this belief. Unless she hits big, the market for this mare's foals will decrease after each disappointing year. By the time the mare reaches 12, she's two years away from being old in many buyers' minds. She could be very difficult to sell and get your money back. Think carefully before investing in this "middle-aged" mare with no successful offspring to her credit.

For mares past the age of 12, the age prejudice can work in your favor. Good mares with good pedigree and production records can often be purchased reasonably because of their advancing age. I've purchased plenty of older mares during my career. It can be a great opportunity to obtain a fine mare. As I have previously noted, many people believe that a mare's best foals are her first five. This theory provides attractive opportunities for the market breeder as well as for those hoping to breed a runner but who don't subscribe to the theory.

You often see good mares put up for sale when they hit 13 to 15 years of age, some with two black-type winners to their credit Their owners are convinced that the mare's best production years are behind her. This can be your chance to acquire some fine, well-bred mares.

There are three steps to follow when evaluating an aged broodmare: (1) Get her complete reproductive history. Find the actual statistics of her getting in foal and delivering a live foal. Know how many covers it took to settle her, and if she is a shy or difficult mare to breed. The teasing records are a valuable source of information. They list the dates she was checked, teased and covered, and describe the results. Has she slipped any foals? Is there a history of chronic infection, or has she had any kind of surgery? Did she have any problems delivering her foal? Did she make enough milk? Know the answers to all these questions before you invest your money in the older broodmare.

(2) Do the research on the farm personnel who cared for her. Have a frank discussion with the farm manager or the mare manager. Talk with the veterinarian who attended her. Be aware of the calibre of the people who cared for the mare. Perhaps you and your excellent veterinarian can improve on this mare's conception rate. If she comes from a top farm, however, you will need a miracle to accomplish what they could not.

(3) Obtain permission for your own veterinarian to conduct a thorough examination, verifying the information you already have. Your veterinarian has last word here. If he concurs with the seller's information, you have a green light. This is standard operating procedure. It is your right to know.

It is impossible to know if the good older mare has already produced her best foal. You can only make an educated guess. But you must not gamble or guess in the area of her reproductive history.

The biggest advantage to the buyer of an older, proven producer is that the mare has an established value. It is possible to look at the value of the stallions she was covered by and the prices at which her foals sold, and determine a value for the mare. For example, if a mare consistently produces foals that sell for $150,000 from stallions of $40,000 seasons, you know she produces sales yearlings. This is a valuable mare, something you can put a price on. Looking past a little age can be a great opportunity to obtain a fine mare, but there are risks. Do your research - don't buy in the dark!

Pocketbook: There probably isn't much I can tell you about your own resources for buying horses. Only you know how deep your pockets are. But over the years I've known some men with mighty deep pockets which were picked clean in the horse business. My advice to you is three-fold:

(1) Determine how big a capital investment you are willing to make. A good Thoroughbred or Standardbred mare will be expensive, but you need to set limits and stick to them. There will always be opportunities to buy horses. Wait for the deal that fits your investment strategy.

(2) Buy quality, not quantity. The initial purchase price of a mare is only the beginning. It will cost anywhere from $7,000 to $12,000 a year to keep the horse. The bad ones cost just as much to keep as the good ones. Consider the economics of owning two good mares, contrasted with owning eight mediocre ones. The odds of producing a good racehorse from those eight mares are poorer than from the two good ones. Meanwhile, your expenses are four times greater with the cheap ones.

(3) Engage the services of a reputable bloodstock agent. His business is providing information to keep you from spending good money on a bad horse. You need specific, "per horse" advice to make the most profitable investment possible.

Buying In-Foal Mares: Breeders are always tempted to speed up the timetable for having foals hit the ground. That is why they are attracted to broodmares that are already in foal. The temptation is reinforced by the fact that the owner of the mare at the time of foaling will be recorded in the registry as the breeder of the foal.

Buying mares in-foal can be a great way to get into the breeding business quickly. A crucial decision has already been made for you. You may benefit from the breeding judgment of the seller, and you may even benefit from another's financial hardship by picking up a pregnant mare at a great price. But there are additional standards by which to judge in-foal mares and there are breeding and buying strategies you must consider. Where there is opportunity, there is also risk.

Covering Sire: Covering sire refers to the stallion to which the in-foal mare was bred. The importance of the covering sire may seem obvious, but there are pitfalls.

Some mares at auction are overbred to make them more attractive. Overbred means that they were bred to a stallion with a season price that vastly exceeds the value of the mare. The resulting foal will probably be worth far less than the stud fee, making such a mating unprofitable for the uninformed buyer.

Mares bred to third and fourth year sires are a special risk. As this mare's yearling comes to market, the first two or three foal crops of the covering sire are now beginning to compile racetrack records. If the stallion's get fail to perform well, the value of his offspring will drop sharply. Yearling buyers will decide very quickly, actually too quickly, that a stallion doesn't produce good racehorses. You don't want to be stuck with a Mr. So-And-So yearling the same year that the market drops out of Mr. So-And-So's horses.

Covering Date: The day that the in-foal mare was covered and consequently became pregnant determines the date she will foal. If she was covered in January or February, well and good. But if she was covered in July she will foal in June and a foal born in June is not an easily marketed yearling. This foal will be considerably smaller and less developed than the February and March foals during its yearling year. Even though this June foal will eventually catch up to the others, buyers will not look at this smaller June yearling.

The mare that foals in June is behind, as is her offspring. It makes no sense to breed her right back - she will only produce another late foal the following year. She must be kept open, or barren, so she can be bred early the following spring to get back on the schedule of producing more saleable foals.

This mare that was covered in July could be a young, healthy, terrific mare and a terrific bargain but I still wouldn't buy her. I would buy a barren mare over one with a July covering date. Be aware of the setback you're buying with this late covering date.

Additional Risks: One of the major problems in the racehorse business is keeping mares in foal. A pregnant mare purchased through an auction is at risk of aborting her foal. Mares will abort their foals for many reasons, one of the major reasons being stress. The preparation for a sale is stressful for the mare because it involves many changes in routine. The mare is taken out of the pasture where she has lived for several months and put up in a stall. Her diet changes from predominantly grass to hay and grain, and she is bathed and blanketed to improve her appearance. Then she is shipped, possibly a long distance, to the sale grounds and put into another new stall. Her feed may again be different and familiar companions are not there. These changes and disruptions all add stress and take their toll. This increases the possibility that the in-foal mare will abort after the commotion and stress of the auction. Now all the buyer has is the mare. If he paid a fancy price for her because of the stallion to which she was bred, it's a real loss.

Broodmares should be bought for their underlying value, not upon the potential value of any foal they carry. Any premium you pay for what she is carrying is money at risk.

High Risk Mares: High-risk mares are those mares that are not likely to produce a foal at a profit in the short-term, and mares that are not likely to produce a quality foal at any time.

Risky mares are low-quality mares, very old mares, over-bred mares, mares bred to third and fourth year sires, mares with late covering dates and mares with poor pedigrees or no racing performance in their backgrounds. Add to the list mares with a history of reproductive health problems, fat mares and mares that have had colic surgery. All these mares are the kind that an uninformed newcomer to the business might buy. There might be a good one in this bunch, but proceed with caution. Get the whole story.

How to Find Broodmare Bargains: Looking for bargains may be compared to looking for beauty that no one else can see. The following situations suggest an opportunity.

An upcoming sale has a nice seven-year-old mare with a solid pedigree, but no racetrack performance to recommend her. Neither of her two foals performed well either. Now every buyer reads the race record and pedigree in the sales catalog, incomplete as it often is. This mare has not attracted much attention from the buyers because of her mediocre production record. But what about the rest of the story on this mare? If you find out why this mare's first two foals didn't race well or at what age her mother or sister produced their best foals, you will have an edge. If you knew that most of her family came from poorly run farms or went to a trainer with a reputation for ruining horses, you'd have some powerful information. I can't stress strongly enough the need for solid research before buying any mare.

I believe that if you do good research, barren mares offer the most consistent opportunities for bargains. The clue is to find out why the mare is barren. Was she poorly managed at the previous farm? Was she bred to a stallion whose potency was on the wane? What is her past history? Has she produced foals regularly and is this her "off" year? Is her owner losing interest in the business and not breeding more foals? Is there a financial problem at the farm?

If the mare is healthy, has a good pedigree and a record for producing foals, I believe buying the barren mare is an attractive option. The key is doing good research on why she is barren.

An underbred mare may present another chance to make a profitable investment. Perhaps the mare's owner is going broke and can't afford the fee of the stallion suitable for a quality mare. A tip-off here is an entire broodmare band in foal to the same stallion, probably Old Fred in the next paddock or the neighbor's horse.

It is always possible that someone has a good mare, but doesn't realize her value. While this doesn't happen every day, if such a situation comes your way, consider it. Sometimes, knowledgeable owners pass away and leave their bloodstock to heirs who may have no interest or knowledge in the business. Anxious to escape the considerable costs of maintaining horses, they may sell the stock at less than market value. The informed investor stands to reap a windfall in undervalued broodmares.

Cheap Mares: The difference between a bargain and a cheap mare is that a bargain is a high-quality mare bought at a good price, while a cheap mare is a low-quality mare at any price.

Every now and then someone asks me about buying a mare for $1,500 or $2,000 and breeding her to Seattle Slew or another top stallion. I always counsel against this, because the stallion won't "pick up" this type of mare very much. If you intend to sell the foal, it is unlikely that you will get back the stud fee. Buyers want to see strength on both the stallion's side and the mare's side. The chances of getting a racehorse from this type of mating are highly remote.

The cost of raising horses is so high and the competition on the racetrack is so tough that I would discourage you from trying to breed with cheap mares. I've seen people at the sales trying to sell their yearlings from low-quality mares. They couldn't afford to have them prepped and no one even looks at them. Many times these breeders can barely afford to truck them back home and it's a sad situation. If they had taken the same money and bought a piece of a good horse, they'd be much further ahead.

My Suggested Investment Strategy: Many buyers consider the maiden mare to be a gamble, but here is a way to stack the odds in your favor if your goal is to breed for the market.

Consider purchasing a stakes-placed filly, out of a decent family, with a price tag of $30,000. Breed her early for the next three years to a promising first or second year sire. No one knows what she will - or if she even can - produce good foals. All this begins to change when the first foal hits the ground. Now she is a producer and, as her foals reach the yearling market and then the racetrack, her reputation is made or lost again. If she produces good racehorses, her value will increase for many years, perhaps to astronomical levels, until she is in her 20s or no longer producing foals. But if her first three or four three foals are disappointments, her value drops sharply and so does the value of her foals. Her race record and her pedigree lose some luster and her value begins to slip.

125

After the third foal is born is the time to decide whether to keep this mare or cull her from your broodmare band. If your $30,000 mare produces three *average* foals, you can probably sell her after the third foal and get $20,000 for her. Assuming you had sold the foals, too, you'd get your money back out of this mare. At this point, you haven't lost money and you're still in the breeding business.

Now factor in a bit more strategy and a bit more luck. Rather than only average-looking foals, she may produce three good-looking, well-conformed foals. Because of her pedigree and race record and because of their looks, these foals may bring around $50,000 each at the sales. If you decided to sell, you could probably get $100,000 for her. You're making money in the breeding business.

Barring accidents and acts of God, this is the kind of investment that won't go too far wrong. With good judgment and a little luck, this strategy can do well for you. The trick is to start with the right raw material and know the timing.

Perhaps you would like to use this strategy, but the stakes-placed filly doesn't fit your pocketbook. There are alternatives. An equally well-bred filly that didn't do much at the track will be more affordable. Her foals will still be attractive to yearling buyers because of her family. You might even find through your research that there was a good reason she didn't do well at the track, such as an injury or bad handling. This is the type of mare that I would look at. She is worth your consideration.

Buying Privately: Buying privately has advantages. The biggest one is time - you have time to look at the horse, research its background and look at it again. And, there is time to negotiate the deal.

In a private sale, you or your agent may already have an established relationship with the seller that may benefit you. Or, one may develop that benefits all parties involved. There is always the possibility of getting more information, or inside information, in a private negotiation.

This is particularly true when buying fillies off the racetrack. Young race mares can frequently be bought at a good price at the track near the end of the season. Owners who do not intend to breed them, particularly those who do not own farms, may prefer to sell them rather than board them until they can get them into a sale. I like to buy mares off the track privately because I can talk to the trainers, riders or drivers and grooms and get the whole story on these mares. If they were offered at auction, it would be more difficult to get their complete history.

Another good strategy for buying privately is to select a number of mares you like from an auction catalog, then check the results of the auction, noting those marked RNA, or Reserve Not Attained. Find the highest bid offered on these horses, then contact their owners and make a somewhat lower offer. It is possible that some of these mares' owners were a bit bold in setting their reserve. What appeared to be a $100,000 mare before the auction may look more like $75,000 now that she's back in the owner's barn.

The disadvantage of buying privately is that the supply of horses for sale is limited. To the inexperienced eye, the animal may appear more valuable than it really is because there are no others with which to compare it. A large sale has hundreds of horses grouped into ages and classes, offering both supply and comparison.

Buying at Auction: The Thoroughbred and Standardbred industries have a long tradition of selling quality breeding stock at public auction. Buying at an auction can be a great opportunity. Another breeder's "culls" could be exactly what you are seeking for your breeding program. The auction is your chance to select from a large number of horses of different ages, classes and prices.

Seeing a large number of horses offered for sale at the same time is more than a convenience. It is a chance to increase one's knowledge of horseflesh and its relative value. A person's eye is naturally better when judging one horse against another, rather than comparing a single horse against an artificial standard.

If the bidding lags behind your expectations, or jumps way beyond them, this does not necessarily mean that your appraisal of the horse's value was wrong. At any auction, you are bidding against the informed buyer and against the "fool." If the bidding goes beyond what you believe the value to be, drop out. In this business, the money will always run out before the opportunity to buy another good horse runs out. View the auction as a free education in market value. The art is in knowing how to interpret that lesson.

Risks of Buying at Auction: Auctions present both opportunities and risks. There is always the possibility of buying a good horse at 60% of its actual value. Bear in mind, however, that every consignor is hoping to sell his horse for 160% of its value. And sometimes this happens. Be aware of the risks built into the auction process.

So many horses, so little time. You must decide what type of horses interest you, what families, what performance records and what price range. If you wait until the auction to do your research, you'll be dazzled by all the black type they manage to put in the catalogs. What is not printed in the auction catalog is at least as important as what is.

You need to know what all the brothers, sisters, half-brothers and so on have sold for and their performance records on the racetrack. The auction catalog will list the stakes-winning colt of the mare you're considering. It will certainly not mention the other seven colts she produced that never even saw the racetrack. The sisters of the dam of the filly you're looking at - what have they produced? Who bred all these horses, who bought them and who trained them? How many broke down and why? Which youngsters have had surgery to correct crooked limbs? Some mares produce straight, correct foals year after year and some do the exact opposite - does this mare fall into the latter category? Which mare has had colic surgery that may shorten her reproductive life? This kind of information can make the difference between a profitable investment and a waste of money.

Finally, be aware that a racehorse auction is an exciting, glamorous event. It's easy to get carried away by the rhythm and romance of the bidding and wind up spending much more than you should. The wise auction buyer uses a four-part strategy: (1) Get the information, (2) know your limit, (3) set your limit, (4) stick to your limit.

Leasing Mares: The alternative to buying a mare is to lease one for a breeding season. The price for leasing a mare for a year is usually 25% of the value of the mare. Select a stallion whose season price corresponds roughly with the lease price. The resulting foal should sell for three times the stud fee, covering both initial investments and giving a profit.

If you have a chance to lease a truly superior mare, the owner may require that she be boarded and foaled at his place to protect his investment. This is not unusual. If you cannot agree to his terms, perhaps a good outside facility devoted to foaling mares would satisfy both parties.

A mare of lesser value, or one belonging to a financially strapped individual, can probably be leased for little or nothing, as long as you agree to provide all the care and expenses associated with her upkeep. If you are considering leasing a mare, make certain that she is worth it. The risks and expenses of good horses are no greater than with cheap ones.

Lease agreements can be as individual as the people entering into them. But the potential for problems is universal. Know what you're getting into and with whom you're dealing. Both parties should discuss two areas thoroughly. Who keeps the mare and who is responsible for the bills? Does she remain with her owner or go with the lessee? What about veterinary bills and extraordinary veterinary bills? Both parties should discuss "what if?" The best environment for the mare should be a primary concern, but what about the mare expecting a $5,000 foal who needs $20,000 in veterinary care to produce it, or to even survive? Any misfortune or neglect that the mare suffers affects both parties adversely. An accident to the mare or foal is tragic. A lawsuit can be disastrous. These are "no-win" situations for both parties and a well-drafted agreement helps to cut losses equitably.

Foal Sharing: Foal sharing is an agreement between the owner of a mare and the owner of an interest in a stallion to share the foals from the union. The owner of the mare often sees foal sharing as a means of breeding his mare to a better stallion than he could otherwise afford. Foal sharing is often done with the manager or owner of a stallion who has an extra season. This is a natural arrangement, since each party can make an investment with no cash. Secretariat was the product of a foal sharing arrangement.

Whether they split the ownership of one foal, or each person gets every other foal, is up the individuals involved. This and the matter of financial responsibility is decided beforehand and usually a contract is drawn up.

Foal sharing carries many of the same risks as leasing mares. It's almost impossible for a contract to provide for all the possibilities and misfortunes that may occur. Consider the case of a foal that dies because of the negligence of a groom hired by one of the parties or the mare that founders due to retained afterbirth and requires thousands of dollars worth of veterinary attention. Imagine the blame and the conflicts over the bills. Enter into these agreements with your eyes wide open.

The way to successful foal-sharing lies in knowing that the agreement is as good as the person with whom you enter into it. It's hard to find a good partner for such an arrangement, but when you find the right person, it can work splendidly.

Chapter 8

Stallion Selection

It is the stallions, rather than the mares, which have had the greatest impact on the breed. This may sound contradictory to what I said in the previous chapter about the importance of the mare and how she contributes 50% of the gene pool to any foal. A mare has great influence on the outcome of individual matings which - at the most - are limited to only eight or 10 foals. A stallion, by contrast, may sire hundreds of foals. His influence is felt among a much larger number of offspring. The stallion is given the opportunity to pass on to future generations his speed, stamina and heart, and has an equal chance to infect them with his conformational flaws.

No one can say with certainty what produces speed in the racehorse. Two horses may appear to be identical in every way. One will go on to be a champion while the other will not run a lick. It is impossible to watch a dozen foals romping in the pasture and decide, "That one will make a great racehorse." Some horses show little promise on the training track but go on to become outstanding performers.

Sometimes the only thing that distinguishes a winner from his better conformed, more royally bred peers is a strong preference for finishing in front. Perhaps it is something psychological, rather than physical, that makes great racehorses. It may be competitiveness, stubbornness, a desire to please or what they refer to as "heart" that makes a winner, not straight legs or good shoulders. To whatever you attribute it, a champion likes to race and he likes to win. He hates to see anyone in front of him. And he'll hang on with all he's got (and maybe more than his legs and lungs can stand) to hold the lead.

Breeders of racehorses since the days of Matchem, Eclipse, Messenger and Hambletonian have known what they want to breed. The question is how to get it.

We know that speed is hereditary. What we don't know is exactly how this occurs. But, sorting out what we know from what we don't know, we see that:

1) You can't tell by looking at a horse whether he will be a good sire. If he is a good sire, it doesn't matter what he looks like.

2) The ultimate test of a stallion, the only test that counts, is what he produces in his foals. If a stallion can produce racehorses that win at the right distance and in the right company, it doesn't matter what he looks like or what his foals look like. His conformation, temperament, height and general appearance are unimportant except to the extent that any one of these items limit his ability to produce foals that win important races. The horse that crosses the finish line first is the superior horse. Period.

Prepotency: A term usually reserved for stallions, *prepotency* is defined as "the greater capacity of one parent to transmit certain characteristics to offspring." A less formal definition is "you can always tell a Round Table horse." A stallion which sires a high percentage of foals as good or better than himself is said to be prepotent.

Unfortunately, it is more difficult to predict the prepotency of a prospective sire than it is to define it. The horse may come from a line of extremely prepotent sires, but fail to stamp his own get. Sometimes a stallion will produce foals better than himself, with no indication in his pedigree that he will do so. We are forced to make an educated guess. The more educated we are, the better we can choose a stallion likely to transmit his own qualities.

The Statistics Game: Racing publications attempt to give insights into the prepotency of sires, or lack of it, by publishing statistics on their offspring. When you start looking at the progeny statistics of stallions, you may be overwhelmed by the volume of information available. Every week *The Thoroughbred Times* and *The Blood-Horse* publish lists of leading Thoroughbred sires. They publish annual reviews and compilations the size of the Manhattan phone book. Pull up a chair, get comfortable and review: the leading sires by current year earnings, by lifetime earnings, sires of 2 year olds and sires of broodmares both current and lifetime, general sire lists, juvenile sire lists, freshman sire lists, etc. The lists chart the size of the foal crop, the number of runners, the number of starts, wins, places and shows, class and distance of races, and money earned. Particular emphasis is placed on the number of stakes winners each stallion has produced. Each list is set up a little differently, so read the fine print.

The common denominator for ranking Thoroughbreds is money earned or stakes winners sired. The process of ranking sires by money won is sometimes arbitrary and misleading. Consider the case of an obscure stallion. This horse never produced a decent racehorse with any mare until one spring when lightning struck. This foal was a statistical anomaly that became a great horse, winning a great deal of money and booting his sire onto the list of leading sires. The only lesson here is that miracles do happen.

In the same vein, a dollar is not always a dollar in racehorse earnings. Was it earned in top company, or was it ground out a $1,000 at a time over several seasons at obscure tracks? Races over a distance often pay more. The earnings of a good sprinter may not reflect his actual value. Some million-dollar earners are not as good as horses that have won less. I recall several horses that passed the $1 million mark in earnings largely through clever management. European horses often win smaller purses and can be much better racehorses than their money-won records suggest.

"Stakes winners" is another misleading phrase. Not all stakes races are created equal. There are the prestigious graded stakes, there are ungraded stakes and there are restricted stakes. Statebred stakes races are examples of restricted stakes. They admit only those horses born in the specified state and nominated to the race. In those states with few racetracks and small racehorse populations, the state-bred competition can be notably soft. The simple phrase "stakes winner" doesn't always tell the whole story.

The Standardbred breeder may have an edge here when ranking stallions. The traditional criteria for ranking Standardbreds is time over a mile, not money earned. Accumulated earnings in unspecified company can be manipulated by clever management, while speed over a set distance is absolute. The only variable is the size of the track. Since it is easier to sustain speed on a longer track than it is on a shorter one, the mile track always has better times than a 5/8 track. But this is easily discovered. With Standardbreds, it's relatively easy to see which are the top horses.

A problem with statistics is that there is a long wait before a pattern emerges. However, a young sire will be known by some to be either a success or a failure long before the statistics are published. By the time a horse is three, his permanent traits are established and his trainer, jockey, exercise rider and groom are starting to talk. If a new sire's colts are brilliant, they'll know it. And if they don't want to run or can't be kept sound, they'll know that, too. If anyone knows why they broke down or wouldn't train, it is the professionals who work with them. You won't get the whole picture without talking to these people.

Breeding Theories: There have been many breeding theories over the years. The nicking theory and the dosage theory are popular worldwide. Nicking is the idea that a particular stallion will be successful when crossed with mares from specific families. Dosage is more complicated, involving certain outstanding stallion lines having specific numerical values. The breeder arranges the matings to attain specific sums of these values. This is just an overview. The theories are somewhat complex and go into great detail.

I've seen the research on all these theories, and I have to respect them. Do they work? Yes and no. Successful breeding is not a completely random event - only rarely does a superior individual result from an accidental or ignorant mating. Consistently producing superior racehorses requires careful study of the families, such as the knowledge and background needed to implement the dosage system. I recommend you study the various breeding theories. There are advisors on every aspect of breeding selection to help you. You can buy pedigree programs for your computer or use mating services to help you research bloodlines, calculate dosage or compile any sort of statistic you might need. While no system of breeding can guarantee success, the breeder who has read the reference books, studied and consulted with experts will be further ahead.

Understanding breeding theories is only the beginning. A pedigree simply cannot contain the full information about an animal. To breed racehorses successfully, you must look at the whole picture.

The Hybrid Nature of Racehorses: It is said that Thoroughbreds and Standardbreds are hybrids. They are not breeds that evolved naturally, such as Arabian horses. They are relatively new, man-made breeds developed by crossing many different breeds and types of horses. By definition, racehorses are hybrids.

The problem with a hybrid is that they are not a new product in total, rather they are made up of many parts transmitted from other breeds. The result is that hybrids seldom breed true. The best example I can give to explain this complex point is hybrid corn. Scientists develop hybrid seed corn by crossing various strains into a single plant. The resulting seed is a hybrid. When the hybrid is planted, a desirable crop results, which is totally different from the parent plants. But if you replant the seed from the hybrid crop, you will not get the same thing you planted. The new crop will be an assortment of corn plants which resemble the parent plants from which the original hybrid seed was developed.

The same is true when breeding racehorses. Out of a crop of 40,000 foals, of which 20,000 are colts, how many will become outstanding sires? One? Two? The odds are great against any stallion becoming an outstanding sire. Almost all are unable to "stamp" their get.

The problem with breeding racehorses is that what you see is not always what you will get. What you see is the physical type of the horse standing in front of you. It is the result of the random arrangement of chromosomes. They could have yielded any of a million combinations, but they happened to combine in such a way to produce this particular horse. This horse has a specific combination of chromosomes, which will recombine with those of the mare he's mated to in any of another million combinations. The result will be - who knows? Like hybrid corn, there is a tendency of racehorses to regress to the norm. And since we are not sure which characteristics are the ones that produce speed, and whether they are dominant, the puzzle increases in complexity.

Type to Type: Your best chance of breeding a good racehorse is to breed type to type. By this, I mean crossing horses of the same basic physical type, ability and quality, rather than crossing contrasting types. It seems that predicting the type of foal that will result from a particular mating is most reliable when both parents are decidedly similar. When parents are dissimilar, the resulting foal is likely to inherit traits which are disproportionate to its size or type.

Here is what I consider when breeding type to type:

(1) *Size, height and substance of the horse:*   The prospective sire should be similar to the mare in size and substance. Size is the height measured in hands and substance is the circumference of cannon bone and depth of trunk. You will find that most successful sires are 16.1 hands or under. At 15.1 hands Northern Dancer is the best-known example of a small stallion, but many of the top sires are under 16 hands. The 15.2 to 16 hand horse fits more mares than the very small or very large horse. Because he is a better match for more mares, he is usually more successful in the breeding shed.

Note the outline of the horse. Some are long and rangy, while others are square and short-coupled. The compact 15.1 hand stallion is best used on mares that are slightly larger than he is and the rangy 17 hand stallion on mares that are a bit smaller. Avoid contrasting sizes. The 17 hand stallion should not be crossed with a 14.3 hand mare. A big, coarse horse should not be crossed with a small, refined one. Add a little height to the small mare, keeping the same basic body type. Add a little refinement to the coarse horse, with the same restriction on body type.

(2) *Distance capacity:*   At what distance did the horse race successfully? This is more complicated than it appears. The rule is to mate like types, but there are right ways and wrong ways to do this.

The trend of the past few years is to breed speed to speed hoping for two-year-old speed and for the horse that excels at about six furlongs.   The problem is that this ignores the real reason some horses do well as two-year-olds, which is because they mature earlier than others. Some horses come into their abilities early in life. Horses that reach their full running capacities as two-year-olds benefit their owners, who pay fewer training bills per purse. The lower costs of training, the generous purses and the soft competition of the two-year-old races all combine to make breeding horses that mature early a financially rewarding strategy. But it fails to take the long view. The horse that is bred to mature early may have the precocious talent to do well at the shorter distances of two-year-old races, where the competition is soft. But for the distances and stiff competition of the races for three-year-olds - including the classics - such a horse is frequently inadequate. This horse seldom lengthens out to race competitively at a mile or 1 1/4 mile as a three-year-old. He was not bred for these distances.

Sometimes this "short" breeding strategy backfires even more, resulting in a horse that is not competitive even at six furlongs. Such a horse is only suited to races of quarter horse distances. Breeding pure speed to pure speed does not often produce a useful horse on the racetrack.

As I discussed earlier, I believe the best breeding strategy is to breed for the mile. If you miss your mark, your horse has a chance to move to longer or shorter distances. The best rule of thumb is to breed for the mile distance, using similar types. The best cross is a mare and a stallion that both excelled at a mile. Here you will find that most prominent sires were successful at a mile. They fit more mares which increases the chances of success.

Not all stallions and mares, however, excelled as milers. What do you do? One solution is to cross a mare that could run 1 1/4 miles with a stallion that was competitive at a mile. The result probably will be at least a six to seven furlong horse, which is a useful horse. You may even get a horse that runs well at a mile or 1 1/4 miles out of this cross. In the same vein, the horse that was a specialist at six furlongs is best crossed with a miler. You lengthen the six furlong horse without sacrificing speed to distance capacity.

(3) *Quality:* What is the value of the horse, how did the horse perform at the racetrack, against what company, what has the horse's

get sold for and how have they performed? The mare that was barely competitive in the lowest claiming ranks should not be put to a stallion that has sired classic winners. Mating a mare that produces $1,500 yearlings to a sire of yearling sale-toppers violates the spirit of type to type. Quality as a restriction is not widely understood. The old maxim, "Breed the best to the best and hope for the best" needs to be expanded. The best horse for a particular mare is a stallion of similar physique and value that improves the mare but isn't so great as to preclude any possible profit from the mating. Ideally, the result will be a foal that has the best qualities of both parents and a value established thus: 25% of the mare's market value plus the stud fee plus expenses plus a reasonable profit. While this may sound cold and unromantic, successful breeders make this calculation when deciding how to breed their mares.

(4) *Exceptions to type to type:* There are exceptions to the rule of breeding type to type. Stallions and mares with the same faults should never be mated. Do not cross bad knees to bad knees, nervous mares to rank-tempered stallions, unsound horses to those that broke down easily. Offset knees reproduce with disgusting predictability. Temperamental horses are hard to train, hard to race and hard to keep sound. A mare intended to be bred to a certain stallion that passes on offset knees or splayed feet, and there are several top horses in this category, must have correct legs and feet.

Look at his previous crops to see what he produces. Some things such as a parrot mouth or a plain head are forgivable. Faults which relate to unsoundness and cause horses to break down should never be forgiven. There are no perfect horses, but you must breed away from your horse's faults.

Do not fall into the trap of believing it is possible to correct a fault by breeding to its counterpart. If you plan to cross a sway-backed mare with a roach-backed stallion in hopes of producing a good top-line, you will be disappointed. You can breed away from faults. You cannot cancel them out.

Inbreeding and Linebreeding: There is much confusion and misunderstanding in the horse business surrounding the terms inbreeding and linebreeding. Talk with a dozen horsemen and you'll come away with a dozen different explanations for these terms. Regardless of how one explains them, the idea behind each explanation is similar. The goal is to manipulate the pedigree of a potential foal in such a way that it will be a superior racehorse. In the end, everyone is talking about the same thing.

Inbreeding: This is simply the mating of relatives. If an ancestor appears more than once in any pedigree, the animal is *inbred*. All Thoroughbreds are inbred because they all trace their origins to three stallions and about 40 foundation mares. It is difficult to go back four generations in a Thoroughbred pedigree without finding common ancestors and past the sixth generation it is virtually impossible. If you go back far enough, some names appear thousands of times in the pedigree of every Thoroughbred.

Standardbreds may have a broader base of ancestors. Until 1933, the criteria for entering a Standardbred in the Stud Book was the horse's ability to trot or pace a mile in 2:30, regardless of parentage. But because of selection, almost all Standardbreds now trace their lineage to one stallion, a Thoroughbred named Messenger. Messenger's influence gained momentum through his sons and grandsons, many of which had more than one cross to him. The Standardbred stud book, like that of the Thoroughbred, is now closed which assures the continuation of inbreeding. Artificial insemination makes the best stallions available to a large number of mares. Over time, this will lead to a greater degree of inbreeding among Standardbreds.

Inbreeding has fixed certain general characteristics in Thoroughbreds and Standardbreds. In a general sense, all Thoroughbreds look alike and all Standardbreds look alike. A man with a skilled eye can look at a horse and say with a high degree of certainty, "That is a Thoroughbred." Inbreeding also has fixed certain general abilities in each breed. Thoroughbreds are genetically programmed to gallop at high speeds over long distances. Standardbreds have been similarly programmed to trot or pace at high speeds for a mile.

Inbreeding by itself is not usually sufficient to accomplish the aims of the racehorse breeder of producing an above average foal because is it not specific enough. By definition, it does not designate the use of *specific* ancestors or the desire to amplify any particular traits. As a result, random inbreeding to increase the number of ancestors-in-common usually does not result in an improvement of the breed. It is generally agreed that the random inbreeding of Thoroughbreds and Standardbreds can do little more than to perpetuate general characteristics and "type."

Indeed, it is impossible to breed a racehorse which is not inbred and this is a cause of concern to some scientists. Some believe that continued inbreeding may actually contribute to a loss of vigor in some of the offspring. It is, for example, believed that inbreeding contributes to the low fertility rate of some Thoroughbreds. But since it is impossible to breed a racehorse that is not inbred, what is one to do?

Linebreeding: In an attempt to produce a superior athlete, breeders frequently turn to a form of inbreeding known as *linebreeding*. On many occasions, linebreeding seems to work. A glance at the pedigrees of current or former stakeswinners will reveal many linebred horses.

Linebreeding is the selection of one or two specific, outstanding horses to occupy several places "close-up" in the pedigree of the prospective offspring. A breeder may choose to linebreed to an outstanding stallion or to an outstanding mare. The idea behind linebreeding is to concentrate the genes of the outstanding horse in a pedigree in the hope that the qualities or traits of the outstanding horse will emerge in the foal. If a superior ancestor appears in more than one place in the pedigree, his (her) genetic contribution to the offspring is increased. It is *much* more likely (both genetics and arithmetic are at work here) that the offspring will inherit at least some of the superior individual's traits. The more places the superior horse occupies in the pedigree, the greater the likelihood that his traits (good and bad) will appear in the offspring. This gives the breeder an element of control and predictability in his breeding program.

The goal in linebreeding is not only to concentrate the genes of a particular horse in a particular pedigree, but to place the superior horse in *specific* places in the pedigree. First, the horse to which you are linebreeding must be "up close" in a prospective pedigree. By up close, I mean within the first five or six generations. Next, the duplicated ancestor must appear in the pedigrees of both the mare and the stallion.

Linebreeding is described using a numerical shorthand or formula. To understand and describe a linebred horse, examine the pedigree for common ancestors. If you see the same name on the top (in the sire's pedigree) and again in the bottom (in the dam's pedigree), the pedigree shows linebreeding. If the same name appears more than once only on the top half of the pedigree, only the sire of the horse is linebred. Perhaps only the bottom of the pedigree has names in common, which means that only the dam is linebred. If the sire is linebred to one particular horse and the dam is linebred to another horse, but sire and dam have no names in common, the resulting horse is an *outcross* between two linebred horses. For a horse to be linebred, his pedigree must show that both parents had ancestors in common. The same name must appear - in any position - on both the top and the bottom of the pedigree.

To describe how the horse is linebred, count the *removes*. Each generation away from the horse you are looking at is one remove - the sire and dam are the first remove, grandsires and grandams are in the second remove, great-grandsires and great-grandams are in the third remove, etc. When you have located the ancestors in common and the removes in which they appear, it's possible to describe how the horse is linebred. Start at the top of the pedigree and work your way down, because sires are always mentioned first. Find the common ancestor and identify his remove, then add an "X" and identify him again by the remove where he next appears.

Imagine you have a horse that is linebred to Mr. So-And-So. Mr. So-And-So is the grandsire on the top and on the bottom. With two grandparents in common, this horse, Tattoo, is linebred 2 X 2 to Mr. So-And-So. The pedigree on the next page illustrates this.

	1st remove	2nd remove
Tattoo	Semper Fi	Mr. So-And-So
		Reveille
	Army Boots	Mr. So-And-So
		Taps

The next imaginary foal is linebred 2 X 3 to horse, "C." Each ancestor-in-common appears in bold-face. Count the occurrence and position of bold-face letters. You see two Cs, one in the 2nd remove and one in the 3rd remove. This foal is linebred to C in a 2 X 3 relationship. Notice that all the ancestors behind C are duplicated as well. This foal is linebred to G in a 3 X 4 relationship and to N in a 4 X 5 and so on for all the bold-faced letters.

	1st Remove	2nd Remove	3rd Remove	4th Remove	5th Remove
				N	
			G		
		C		**O**	
				P	
			H		
	A			**Q**	
				R	
			I		
		D		S	
				T	
			J		
Subject Foal				U	
				V	
			K		
		E		W	
				X	
			L		
	B			Y	
				G	**N**
			C		**O**
		F		**H**	**P**
					Q
				Z	
			M		
				A A	

While this formula is accurate, it is not a full description of how the horse is linebred. It does not tell us if the ancestor to which the horse is linebred is a stallion or a mare. Nor is it specific past the 2nd remove - a stallion which is represented by 4 in a 4 X 5 relationship could be in any of four places in the top of the pedigree and in any of five positions in the bottom.

My Formula for Linebreeding: Linebreeding is most successful when two ingredients come together: (1) sound, superior individuals are used in positions close enough to effectively concentrate their genetic material but not as close as *close-breeding*, which is mating brother and sister, father and daughter. The blood of the superior horse is concentrated in the offspring, but the chance of reproducing weaknesses or defects is much less than a closer cross would produce. (2) I look for champions or near-champions that were nearly perfect individuals. I know that if I have soundness, I'll have speed.

When I decide to linebreed, I look at four factors: (1) speed, or racing talent; (2) soundness; (3) workable temperament; and, (4) history of success or failure - has this cross worked previously and how well.

The process must start with qualities you hope to concentrate, the most important being speed. There is no point in concentrating bloodlines if you're not concentrating talent. You can't concentrate the blood of a horse with "the slows" and expect to get a racehorse. If crossing champion to champion is too expensive, it is possible to move away one generation and still expect good results.

Soundness is maintained by avoiding unsoundness. The concentration of inbred genetic material that has produced speed in the last three centuries also has produced faults and weaknesses. When you load the pedigree with good qualities, you risk concentrating the bad points as well. To qualify for linebreeding, each generation should have proved its soundness by racing. Avoid linebreeding horses that break down easily. Concentrating this tendency is a recipe for disaster. Be certain you are not doubling the chance of some defect appearing.

Temperament requires the same restriction as soundness. It is more of an issue with some horseman than others. It's easy to look past a poor temperament if you don't have to handle the animal. But anyone who plans to race must consider temperament when choosing a stallion. Loading the pedigree with nervous horses may produce a nut that can't be trained. A belligerent horse may injure himself fighting his handlers. He is often difficult to train and to ride in a race. A neurotic temperament keeps a horse from realizing his full potential. A good temperament must be there to justify linebreeding.

Finally, has this cross worked before? If the cross has been a success in the past, producing good performers with an absence of defects, you have a green light. If it has not been proven, look very carefully at the above factors.

The biggest obstacle to successful linebreeding is the time it takes to determine a good cross. By the time there are enough horses on the racetrack that are the result of a good linebred cross, their sire is old and their dams are old. We know how to breed Buckpasser mares. We have the combinations that work. What about Alydar mares? We won't have the statistical information for several years. Some combinations are tried so infrequently that there will never be enough offspring to establish any conclusions. No one can produce any valid figures if there are not enough subjects to study.

Good linebreeding is not a guarantee of success, it's a tool. It will work best if you remember to weight all the names on the pedigree equally, making racing performance in each generation the deciding factor.

Practical Breeding Guidelines: In addition to breeding theories, there are practical considerations which must be confronted when choosing a stallion. Few breeders can afford to disregard the pragmatic issues of money, distance and market trends. Breeding is most successful when theory is balanced against practical business decisions.

The racehorse market, however, has gone through some profound changes in the past 15 years. These changes continue to alter and shape the market. I will outline some breeding strategies to help you make your selection based on practical business considerations.

(1) *Don't overbreed the mare.* The price of a stallion season and its relationship to the price of a broodmare must be viewed in terms of the potential value of the offspring. Select a stallion based on how the price of his season corresponds to the value of the mare. Even if you have no financial limitations, factor price into breeding decisions to make the best use of a particular mare. For many years, there was a reliable formula for doing this. The rule of thumb was the price of the season should be 25% - 35% of the value of the mare. A mare valued at $30,000 would be appropriately mated with stallions whose seasons range from $7,500 to $10,500.

Consider the fictitious example of a mare worth $10,000 bred to a classic sire for the sum of $100,000. If she is a five and he is a 10 on a scale of value, the foal will likely be a 7 1/2. However, if this mare is bred to a son of the classic sire for $3,000, the result is probably a 6 1/2. The difference between 6 1/2 and 7 1/2 does not approach the difference between $100,000 and $3,000. Buying a $100,000 season for a $10,000 mare is usually a waste of money because most stallions will not improve on a mare that much. This is overbreeding and it's the kind of mistake someone new to the business might make.

Avoiding overbreeding requires you to evaluate your mare's value objectively. It may be difficult to admit that a mare which cost you $50,000 is only worth $10,000. But all successful breeders re-evaluate their stock periodically and adjust their opinions to make the best breeding decisions.

(2) *Don't Underbreed the Mare by Underestimating Her Value.* A mare that sold for $150,000 at Keeneland does not necessarily have to be restricted to a $50,000 horse. If she's an exceptional mare, you may want to pay more and get the best horse available or take a chance on the most promising first-year sire. With mares' prices headed down, a truly valuable mare is all the more rare and valuable. Don't underbreed this mare.

An old mare, 18 or 19 perhaps, may have little value in the sales ring. No one will pay much for a mare of this advanced age. Her value cannot be judged on her sales value, but rather on the potential for the type of foal she may deliver. If this is a good mare that has produced some quality foals, she should be booked to a superior stallion. The genes are there to produce at least one more quality foal. Don't waste this good mare by using a stallion whose season would match her unrealistically low market value. This mare is worth the investment of booking a good horse.

(3) *Watch the trends of the yearling market.* Your objective is to calculate the potential value of the offspring of any breeding. The market now favors good conformation over pedigree, and first- and second-year sires are popular. It is possible to breed to a first-year horse for $10,000 and, if the foal becomes a good-looking yearling, sell it for more than a yearling from a $50,000 horse.

4) *Don't overlook a bargain.* If you have the chance to breed to an outstanding stallion at a bargain price, don't let an outdated formula stand in the way of opportunity. European horses can be particularly good bargains in terms of stud fees. European horses may earn less on the track than their American counterparts. While they may stand for less money, they're just as good racehorses, and sometimes better.

5) *A new formula.* Not all stallions stand for their true value. Some cost twice what they should and a few are undervalued. Set an objective value for your mare and find the horse that complements her, with a price that complements her value - make your own formula.

6) *Breeding based on location.* Location is not an issue for breeders who live in Kentucky, Florida, California or other centers of racehorse breeding. But the breeder who lives in Minnesota or Montana must factor into the equation the cost of shipping his mare long-distance and boarding her for several months. The selling price of the resulting foal must absorb this extra expense to make a profit. The broodmare of only moderate value does not warrant the added expense of being shipped halfway across the country to be bred. Her owner should find a decent stallion in his part of the country to keep expenses from overtaking the possible profit.

7) *Breeding based on fertility.* Consider fertility when choosing a stallion. Learn what his conception rate is, his average number of covers and how long his sperm live. If his fertility is low and it requires multiple covers to achieve conception, you must consider this risk. Such a stallion may be good choice for a healthy, young mare. But this stallion is not an acceptable risk for an older mare with a history of reproductive problems.

Established Stallions Versus New, Unproven Stallions: The safest choice for picking a stallion is to book a proven sire for your mare. The greatest recommendation for any stallion is his record of production. Breed to this year's Derby winner and the only thing you can be sure of getting is a foal from this year's Derby winner. Breed to a stallion with a history of producing good racehorses and you substantially increase your chances of getting a winner.

There are many older stallions of near-classic stature, in a range of prices, that will produce a foal for racing or for the sales ring. The progeny of such stallions have a record of sales prices and racing performance to which you can refer. Put to a mare of appropriate quality and value, they should produce a foal worthy of your investment dollar. Their yearlings will bring respectable prices. They *are* the best choice for producing racehorses that enhance your mare's value.

First-Year Stallions: If you are willing to accept greater risk, choose an unproven, first-year stallion. It's exciting when a new stallion's first foals arrive and you may get in on the ground floor of something big. Well-conformed offspring of a first- or second-year sire will often outsell those of a proven horse.

The first judgment of a stallion's abilities as a potential sire are made when his first foals hit the ground. Here, prepotency is a double-edged sword. These foals may have inherited the strengths of the sire, but it's every bit as likely that they have his weaknesses. The breeder intending to sell his yearlings must look carefully at the conformation of the foals from this young stallion. Stallions that improve the conformation of the mares they bred have justified the market breeder's gamble.

Foals eventually turn into yearlings and are evaluated again. Now there is more information about the sire's ability to reproduce his own type. By this age, a few awkward, weak foals will have redeemed themselves. Veterinary science and good management will have saved several more from being conformational rejects and only those breeders and buyers with inside information will know which ones.

The rest of the world waits for the stallion's first two crops to reach the racetrack. By the time the colts are two- and three-year-olds their race records are public record.

Four Ways to Acquire Stallion Services: There are four ways to acquire stallion services. (1) Stand your own stallion; (2) purchase a stallion season; (3) purchase a stallion share; or, (4) enter into a stallion partnership.

Standing Your Own Stallion: There is always the temptation to stand your own stallion. The cost of boarding a stallion is less than the cost of acquiring stallion services through other means. Some people try to stand a stallion simply because they've become emotionally attached to the horse. Unfortunately, there are many problems associated with standing your own stallion.

First, a good stallion prospect is usually a horse with a good race record. His pedigree must have sufficient strength to suggest that he will be more than a mediocre sire. His sire and grandsire were sires of good racehorses, too. The stallion prospect that meets these specifications is usually not affordable for the individual investor.

While the expense of maintaining a stallion is usually less than that of acquiring services, the expenses of promoting a stallion will quickly overtake any savings. Advertising is expensive but necessary to promote the horse and his foals. The stallion's yearlings will not bring good prices at auction unless the stallion and his get are promoted aggressively.

The biggest risk of standing your own stallion is that of putting all your eggs in one basket. Many horses enter stud each year, but only a handful succeed. Unless the stallion you stand is successful and is a good "product" for other breeders, he will limit your breeding strategies. No single stallion is a suitable mate for all mares and you will be limited to the type of mare that fits him. You probably won't want to breed the stallion's daughters back to him and new mares will be needed to continue your breeding program. The deals and agreements that allow you to breed your stallion's daughters to other quality stallions are only possible if you have a superior horse to start with. Federico Tesio explained why he never stood his own stallion by saying that, if the horse were any good, everyone would want to breed to him and you would simply sell all the seasons. If the horse was not any good, no one would buy his seasons and you would end up breeding to him yourself. Either way, you lose. If the stallion you are considering standing cannot make it on his own in the market place, he doesn't belong in your breeding shed.

Breeding is a risky process. You will spread out your risk by using a combination of both proven and promising young sires. In other words, use all the resources of the stallion market.

Stallion Seasons: Purchasing a stallion *season* means paying a fee to breed one mare to a particular stallion during one breeding season. Depending on the terms of the agreement, it may guarantee you the right to have your mare covered until she produces a live foal as the result of the mating or it may not. After the terms of the agreement have been satisfied, the relationship is over unless a new season is purchased.

Seasons are structured as *Live Foal Guarantee* or as *No Guarantee*. *Live Foal Guarantee* is exactly what it sounds like - if your mare aborts or, for any reason, you don't get a live foal that stands and nurses, you are guaranteed a refund of your money. The stallion or syndicate manager will write you a check. This is not the same as a return privilege. The agreement ends with the breeding season and a new one must be negotiated for the following year. You pay for the season around September 15, when the mare is usually pronounced in foal or when the foal stands and nurses, depending on the way the agreement is written. If she is empty, no fee is due. This is the most expensive way to purchase a season.

No Guarantee is less expensive but has more risk attached. For a discount of about 30% off the cost of a Live Foal Guarantee season, you buy the right to have your mare bred to a particular stallion for that season. The fee is due upfront. If the mare does not conceive that season or if she aborts later, there is no refund. A *No Guarantee* season is a good choice if the stallion has a high conception rate and your mare usually conceives on the first cover. Used with older mares or less fertile horses, it becomes much riskier. If your mare is hard to get in foal, you could lose the entire fee if she has not conceived by the end of the season. The stallion manager also hopes that the *No Guarantee* mare is fertile. He wants to avoid "using up" his horse on a less-fertile mare that may require multiple covers during that season.

Live Foal Guarantee and *No Guarantee* are common arrangements but, depending on the age and quality of the stallion, they may be structured somewhat differently. Some specify a certain number of covers or have other restrictions attached. Do not assume that all *Live Foal Guarantee* and *No Guarantee* agreements are alike. Read the fine print in the breeding contract or have a professional evaluate it for you. Make sure you understand the obligations and risks involved.

Stallion Shares: A stallion share is an ownership interest in a stallion, along with other horsemen. Stallions are usually owned by 40 shareholders, each with a breeding privilege to use or to sell. The relationship confers ownership for the life of the stallion.

John Gaines changed the way many of the best stallions are owned when he convinced the Securities and Exchange Commission that stallion syndications may be structured so they are exempt from securities laws. Prior to Gaines' action in 1977, a group wanting to form a syndicate for joint stallion ownership first needed to comply with the rules regarding the creation of securities. This was a lengthy and expensive process involving things like writing prospectuses and registering the offering with the SEC.

Gaines argued that the securities laws were intended to protect prospective investors who hoped to make a profit through the efforts of the promoter. He said that owning a share in a stallion was different. He proposed to sell shares in stallions, based not upon the expectation of making a profit, but rather for the mutual use of the stallion by the shareholders. He proposed that each shareholder be entitled to one breeding annually for each share owned. The shareholder could breed his own mare to the stallion, give the breeding to a friend, sell the breeding or not use it at all. All shareholders would jointly share in the expenses incurred by owning the stallion. The shareholder may end the relationship by selling his share, but within the terms stipulated by the group of shareholders. Most syndicates specify that other shareholders have the right of first refusal.

The owner of a stallion share must pay his pro-rata portion of the stallion's expenses for the year. The average cost per shareholder runs about $1,000 to $2,500. This seems steep, but consider that the average annual board for a stallion runs $18,000 to $22,000. Add in all the other expenses, including veterinary care, farrier services, insurance, advertising and promotion, nominations for the Breeders Cup or the Breeders Crown, etc. and the total adds up quickly. While the range of syndicate expenses can run from a few hundred dollars to $5,000 or more per shareholder, younger stallions will be at the high end because of more aggressive promotional expenses.

Sometimes a stallion is capable of servicing more mares than there are shareholders. The syndicate may then decide to declare a few bonus seasons. Since there will be fewer bonus seasons than there are shareholders, bonus seasons are allocated by lot. Usually 10 shareholders will get bonus seasons one year, 10 the next, and so on, taking four years to complete the cycle.

Drawing lots for bonus seasons of a stallion that is heading up or heading down in value is a system of chance. If the horse is appreciating in value, the first bonus recipients will not profit as much as those drawing three years later. The situation is much worse for shareholders receiving third-year bonus seasons for a stallion on the decline. The sale of the bonus seasons at fire-sale prices can accelerate the horse's loss of value.

The stallion is under the control of the syndicate manager. The syndicate manager is in charge of caring for the stallion on a day-by-day basis, deciding at what farm the stallion will stand, booking the mares that will be bred, arranging the advertising and promotion, paying the bills and collecting from each of the members the pro rata expenses of running the syndicate. The syndicate manager usually is given four breeding rights per season as compensation for his services.

Partnerships: In the past few years, partnerships have become a popular vehicle for owning stallions. Any number of people may form a partnership but most are between three and 10 individuals. Unlike syndicates, the purpose of a partnership is to make money selling seasons. Partnerships vary as much as the individuals involved. A partnership may divide the breedings among its members or each partner may have to purchase his season, depending on the agreement. Every stallion partnership agreement has varying degrees of responsibility, risk and chance for financial gain.

Stallion partnerships are set up as general partnerships to structure the ownership in a way that may increase tax benefits. The partners make all decisions regarding the management of the stallion and the sale of his seasons. The sale of extra seasons or deals for volume breeding contracts may be decided and executed quickly by a partnership. The profits and the risks are shared by all.

While partnerships can be an excellent way of owning a stallion - I have invested in such arrangements myself - there are drawbacks. Successful investment in a partnership demands a great deal of knowledge and sophistication from the prospective investor. In addition to the quality of the stallion, much depends on a thorough understanding of how the partnership is set up and the calibre of the people that form the partnership. Examine every partnership agreement carefully and have your accountant and your lawyer examine it, too. Understand what benefits and liabilities the agreement confers on you.

From the standpoint of the industry, the trend toward partnerships and away from syndication may not be entirely healthy. Buying a share in a horse was something the new man in the business understood - it encouraged new investments. Partnerships are far more complex.

How to Find Stallion Seasons and Shares: There are two times when stallion shares are offered for sale. Shares are offered for the first time when the syndication is initially established. Later on, it might be possible to purchase the share of an owner who wants to sell out.

For most stallions, you will pay the highest price per share at the time of the original syndication. This is soon after the horse's retirement from the racetrack and when expectations are highest for him. Shares are usually priced about three times the advertised stud fee. Because the stallion was an excellent racehorse, his first few crops of foals will sell for a high price. Usually, owners of newly syndicated "big-name" horses can sell their seasons for a good price or breed their own mare and sell the foal for a good price.

Most initial prices for stallion shares are inflated, considering how few stallions prove to be exceptional sires. Soon after a sire's progeny begin to race, the value of his shares begin to adjust. In the case of exceptional sires, the prices go up dramatically. The lucky few who got in on the ground floor profit handsomely. Unfortunately, the price of most go down. However, this is not usually calamitous for the shareholder. With some luck, he got his mares in foal to this horse and sold the yearlings for the good prices that a first- or second-year sire usually commands.

Purchasing a stallion season or share is as simple as giving the syndicate manager a call. He is the first person to know when any of his shareholders offer their seasons for sale or want to sell their shares.

If you are unable to make an agreement with the syndicate manager for a season or share, use a bloodstock agent. A good bloodstock agent has many contacts and may be able to negotiate a sale for you. He may be able to persuade a shareowner to sell his season. He will know of other stallions which are priced reasonably according to their value and may be good alternative choices. And he will know which stallions aren't stopping their mares, a fact that is not always common knowledge, but which adds to the risk of your investment.

One word of caution when purchasing seasons and shares through agents - beware of agents who offer seasons that you never seem to be able to buy. A few agents will advertise a season to a top horse at a great price, but when you call to inquire about this fantastic deal you're told that it has just been sold. Hear this often enough and you begin to wonder if the agent ever had the season in the first place. As in any other business, if it seems too good to be true, it probably is.

Investing in Proven Stallion Shares: The market for racehorses is a fickle one. The prices for yearlings, seasons and shares are often based more on fashion than underlying value. A sire can become fashionable based upon good publicity or some success over the short term. At the same time, the proven sire - one who has consistently produced superior runners - may fall out of favor in the marketplace. The market value of his seasons and shares will plateau as will the market value of his foals. Notice that I said "market value," not true value. There is a difference.

If your goal is to breed horses for racing, one of your best investments is shares in proven, older sires. The stallion that's a good buy is the near-classic horse that is 17 years old, that has consistently been a top sire and whose stud fee has dropped from $75,000 down to, say, $40,000. Shares in this type of stallion typically sell for 1 1/2 or two times the price of a season. You may find a share in this horse for $60,000-$80,000 from someone who is moving on to another stallion. These are exceptional buys for the person who wants to breed good racehorses while at the same time seeking to minimize his risk. You can sell a season right then for $40,000 and have only $20,000 or $40,000 left in him. The next year that season probably will stay at $40,000 again and this horse will probably live for four or five more years. He's already a proven horse and, more than likely, he is not going to skyrocket in value but the bottom won't fall out of him either. But don't buy them too old. Try to buy them under 18 years.

On the other hand, the value of the semi-proven horse is volatile. If you pay $150,000 for a semi-proven horse that has sired a only few good horses and who is standing for $50,000, the next year he may sire nothing. He might drop right back down. You may be stuck with a $5,000 season which cost you $150,000 a share because you bought at an inflated price.

Semi-proven or middle-of-the-road horses are very risky. A newcomer might get into the business with the semi-proven horse because he doesn't know what he's buying. Thinking that he's getting in for half price, he doesn't realize that the horse's value is as likely to go down as it is to go up.

I believe that it's safer to go with either a brand-new horse or an older, proven horse. First-year sires are good if you get in at a good price. Proven horses, over 10 years old, hold their value or come up slightly. The older stallion gives you statistics to look at and confidence that they're not going to change very much. Chart the prices that the horse's yearlings have brought over the years - unless the horse dies before you can use the first season, you'll get at least that much out of him.

Buying Stallion Seasons and Shares at a Discount: A sure sign that the industry is changing is the availability of stallion seasons and shares for sale at public auction. This would never have happened 10 years ago. Now there are at least two companies that conduct auctions of stallion shares and anyone can find out what a share of Mr. So-And-So is going for on the open market.

Share auctions have not been popular with stallion owners. Some claim it's because it made them tell the truth, so to speak. But there are two sides to the story.

The auctions of stallion shares came along at a time when the prices of many shares were inflated, some to ridiculous proportions. Those inflated shares rose even higher at the first auctions. Conducted in a festive mood, these auctions seemed to encourage excess. While seasoned auction buyers are inoculated against the dizzying effects of champagne and large sums of money, those investors with less experience succumbed to the show business atmosphere. Of course, the bloom faded and the inevitable correction occurred.

There were casualties from the correction. The shareholder who bought his $250,000 share was understandably dismayed when it only fetched $100,000 at auction. While the price was probably inflated, that knowledge didn't make the loss of innocence any less painful. Other stallion shareholders watched the demand for their stallion's shares and services disappear after it was publicly revealed that their value was falling on the auction scene. Such a reversal commonly occurs when a stallion's get perform poorly at the track.

But a few unfortunate people saw their horse's value ruined on what was barely more than a rumor. To make matters worse, syndicate members would sit back and let their stallion's shares sell for 25% of their actual value, knowing they could pick up the share later as per their syndicate's first right of refusal. And who could blame them? It was a no-win situation for everyone involved. I have seen stallions all but ruined and many people badly hurt in such situations and most of the time, it was undeserved.

Stallion people responded quickly to protect their horses' value. It is now the practice of some syndicate managers to attend every auction and bid their horses up, particularly if the horse is on a decline. There is nothing illegal about this practice, but be aware that some part of a stallion's value at these auctions could be the syndicate manager protecting his horse.

Stallion people feel that the value of seasons are skewed by the time of year the auctions are held. In July, they reason, no one has cash for stallion seasons which can't be used until next year anyway. They feel that the same share will sell for more in January than it will in July. Sometimes this is true and sometimes the opposite proves true. Seasons from a stallion that was "hot" last year may sell for a great price in July. If the horse goes from that July to next January without a runner, the seasons will be worth less in January than they were the previous summer.

What conclusions can you make from the unstable picture I have drawn? Two: 1) Auction prices do not always reflect market value, and; 2) auctions seldom hurt the horse on the way up, but often damage the horse on the decline. Knowing these facts will help you to be on the right side of any auction transaction.

Most new syndications prohibit the sale of shares at auction. Others require the seller to put a reserve on the sale. Most of the shares offered at auction are now for older, proven horses with relatively stable values and these shares are being priced more realistically. Now people understand share auctions for what they are and what they aren't.

The positive side of these auctions is that they function independently of the usual network of personal contacts and relationships. New investors are encouraged because everyone has a shot at getting the bargain that appears every once in a while.

Artificial Insemination: The Thoroughbred industry doesn't use artificial insemination. The Jockey Club won't allow it. But I have some thoughts regarding A.I. from my years with Standardbreds and I think it may provide a lesson for the Thoroughbred breeder. It involves improving a breed of racehorses and how those horses are valued.

The Standardbred industry permits A.I. and since its introduction, racing times have improved dramatically. Some of the increase in speed may be attributed to faster tracks. Certainly, the racetracks have improved. But the Thoroughbreds are running pretty much at the same speed they did 30 years ago. They haven't improved like Standardbreds have and I think Standardbreds owe this improvement to A. I. Consider that the best Thoroughbred stallion only gets about 40 mares a season. The top Standardbred stallion can serve 300 mares or more and he'll get all the best mares. The Standardbred breeder can breed champion to champion and I think this has produced a vastly better racehorse in a short amount of time.

The advances in speed and quality as a result of A.I. are a double-edged sword for the Standardbred breeder. He now has access to the top stallions for his mares. But stud duty is reserved for only the truly outstanding trotter or pacer. There is no market for the merely good colt that would have gone to stud 40 years ago. The Standardbred breeder must make all his money at the racetrack, since the odds are that his colt won't make it to stud.

Some years ago, I knew a gentleman who had the fastest band of Standardbred mares in the world. Their average record was 2:02! Today, the good racehorses go in the low 1:50s and a two-year-old has even gone in 1:55, but at the time, those were top-quality mares.

A few years later, this same gentleman and an associate went to Harrisburg, Pa., to buy colts. They bought four of the best-bred yearling colts in the country, paying about $250,000 a piece for them. The following year, one colt compiled the fifth-best race record in the entire country. When their owner decided to sell these colts, he couldn't get any more for them as stallion prospects than what he had paid for them, even for the best one. He said he couldn't believe that he had one of the top trotting colts in the country and couldn't sell him for more than he paid for him as a yearling. He never bought another Standardbred yearling.

Now you know what has happened to the value of Standardbreds. On the other hand, the Thoroughbred's value has held up. People know if they have a really good one they can bring him back as a stallion or sell him and make money. The supply is limited, so you can feel confident about the value of a good Thoroughbred.

Part III

Horse Farm Management

Chapter 9

Broodmare Management

Racehorses are one of the most difficult animals to manage in reproduction. Your biggest challenge as a breeder is to have your mare give birth to a live foal. On average, only about 56% of all Thoroughbred mares which are bred actually give birth to a live foal. Standardbreds have a slightly higher rate of about 65%. Many breedings never "catch." Others catch, but the fetus is aborted for one reason or another. A well-managed broodmare has a far better chance of delivering a live foal than the average mare. Well-managed farms have conception rates of 90% or more and a live foal rate of 80% or more.

Many breeding problems are a result of our impatience with the way nature intended things to be. Racing authorities have established January 1 as the birthday for all racehorses regardless of the actual date on which they are born. It is necessary to begin breeding mares in the middle of February to have our foals be born as soon after January 1 as possible. Foals born in the late spring or early summer are at a disadvantage in their two-year-old and early in their three-year-old years when racing against horses their "same age" which were born months earlier. Nature never intended for a horse to be bred in February. Every time we attempt to breed in February, we are fighting nature.

As horses have evolved, a mare's most fertile period is in May and June. Winter is hard on horses living in the wild. Food is hard to find. Both mares and stallions lose weight over the winter. The short hours of daylight make them less active and every system is directed toward self-maintenance and self-preservation. This is not a time when horses breed naturally.

But soon spring arrives. As the days get longer, the horses become more active. Food becomes more abundant and the mares begin to regain their "bloom." They are no longer merely attempting to stay alive. The mares begin to accept the stallion and are bred when they are on the upward curve, regaining weight and strength.

To breed horses that will satisfy the rules of racing means that we must first frustrate the rules of nature. In February, we must "trick" the systems of the mare into believing that it is late May or June. We must convince nature that the mare has just ended a long winter during which she has lost weight and that she is now on the way back to regaining her normal summer "bloom." And, we must satisfy all of nature's other concerns that this animal is *"breeding sound."* As you might guess, fooling nature can be a touchy business.

Getting a mare into foal according to the rules of nature - and keeping her that way - generally consists of a four-part strategy:

(1) Determine that the mare is breeding sound and eliminate any infections or other health problems of the reproductive system (or of any other system).

(2) In the fall, reduce the weight of the mare to replicate the natural weight loss she would encounter if living in the wild. As the breeding season approaches, reverse the procedure and slowly begin to put weight back on her.

(3) Artificially make the days longer - as if it were spring - by standing the mare under lights.

(4) Breed her at exactly the right moment in her heat cycle, which is just before she ovulates. We must predict the time of ovulation. Although the mare may accept the stallion for as long as a 10-day period, the most effective time to breed is just before ovulation occurs. The objective is to breed her only once, as soon after February 15 as possible, and to have that one breeding result in conception.

Diagnostic Exams to Determine Breeding Soundness: Before buying any mare, you must determine that she is *breeding sound*. Making sure she stays that way is a continuing program. *Breeding sound* means that she does not have an infection in her uterus, that her reproductive organs are fully developed and healthy, and that her cervix and vagina have no injuries or malformations. In short, *breeding sound* means the mare is in good general health with no discernible reason that she cannot conceive, carry and deliver a foal.

There are five diagnostic techniques that are widely used to determine breeding soundness and to manage the breeding strategy for individual mares. These techniques have dramatically increased our ability to recognize and treat infertility and to predict the time of ovulation.

Palpating: There are a number of reasons for palpating a mare. Palpation is used as part of an examination for breeding soundness to determine whether her reproductive organs are normal, healthy and free from injury or malformation. It is used again prior to breeding to predict the approximate time of ovulation and again, after breeding, to confirm that ovulation has occurred. Later in the pregnancy, palpation is used to determine the status of a variety of conditions.

To palpate means "to touch." The veterinarian puts on a long surgical glove up to his shoulder and gently inserts his arm into the mare's rectum. The examination or "palpation" takes place with only the thin intestinal wall separating the examiner's hand from the organ being examined. The veterinarian examines the uterus for size and tone, and checks the ovaries to determine the presence and stage of the follicle, or egg sac. A skilled veterinarian with good technical training and experience can feel at what stage the mare is in her cycle. Knowing when she will come into heat, he can recommend when to culture her, when to check her again and, after a series of palpations, when to breed her.

Conducted by an experienced, competent veterinarian, palpation is a valuable broodmare management tool that is relatively non-invasive. The vagina is never entered, reducing the chance of contamination or infection. But palpation has attendant risks. The intestinal wall of the horse is fragile. The possibility of a tear is remote, but it exists, even with the most experienced examiner. Considering how frequently a mare is palpated, the possibility of tearing the intestinal wall is a concern.

The danger of being kicked is great for the examiner. Restrain the mare properly with a twitch, stocks or sedation. Alternatively, the mare may be backed into a doorway or behind a stout Dutch door to prevent the veterinarian from being kicked. Some veterinarians will refuse to palpate the mare if there are no facilities for doing it safely, and rightly so. The proper safety measures protect both mares and humans.

Culturing: A common cause of mare infertility is infection of the uterus. A mare may appear to be healthy in every way but if she is infected or "dirty," it is unlikely that she will conceive or give birth to a live foal. A continuing program for detecting infections in mares is essential.

Taking a culture of the uterus is the diagnostic tool used to determine if a mare is infected and, if she is, to identify the type of infection. This test is usually performed when the mare is in heat and her cervix is open. Some veterinarians will not attempt to culture a mare unless she is in heat. Others feel that they can obtain a good culture at any point in the mare's cycle. If your veterinarian is of the first school, a culture can only be performed every 21 days or however frequently the mare comes into heat.

The veterinarian performs the test by passing a sterile swab through the cervix, carefully touching the mucus lining of the uterus with the swab. The mucus on the swab is sent to a lab where any bacteria present are put into a culture medium and allowed time to grow. The sample is then checked and the bacteria identified. Culture results are usually known within 24 to 48 hours. If an infection is found, your veterinarian will prescribe the appropriate treatment and the mare will be cultured again in three weeks.

Maiden and barren mares are cultured in late summer or early fall, and again in December before the breeding season. Do this early because you will need a lot of time to clear up the problem if the mare is infected. You must have clean cultures going into January to take advantage of the accelerated breeding season. Even in December, most veterinarians can determine when the mare has sufficient heat to permit the culture swab to pass through the cervix. It is not necessary that she ovulate for a successful culture.

Vaginal Speculum Examinations: Visual examination of the vagina and cervix of the mare is done with a speculum. The speculum is a smooth, blunt instrument that is inserted through the lips of the vulva, then opened to allow the veterinarian to view the vagina and cervix. This procedure is done under the most sterile conditions possible, with the mare thoroughly scrubbed and all tail hair bandaged and out of the way.

Every new mare is given a speculum exam (called a "spec," in veterinary shorthand) when she arrives on the farm. If she is a maiden, the veterinarian looks for normal development of the organs and the appearance of healthy tissues. A barren mare is examined for the presence of tears, adhesions or similar injuries that must be repaired before she can be bred.

All mares are given a speculum exam at eight or nine days after foaling. The veterinarian must determine whether the mare has suffered any damage from foaling, such as bruising, that needs time to heal or if there has been any tearing of the cervix or vagina that must be repaired. The veterinarian also looks for any abnormal discharge or off-color tissue indicating that the mare should not be bred on her foal heat or on the subsequent heat.

The speculum exam is a not a substitute for culturing or vice versa. Both are important routine procedures that help the veterinarian decide if the mare has the green light to go ahead and be bred or if she needs treatment.

Ultrasound: Ultrasound is a fairly recent diagnostic tool that has proven helpful in problem mares as well as pregnant mares. The ultrasound examination is performed using a rectal probe. The probe "reads" the reproductive organs through the intestinal wall, then sends the information back to a monitor that displays a moving picture of the organs as they are being examined.

A mare that cultures clean but does not get in foal should be checked by ultrasound to help determine the reason for her subfertility. Ultrasound can "see" problems that a culture might miss. The uterus has folds that can hide a pocket of infection - the culture medium cannot grow what the swab did not reach. The ultrasound will pick up and display any pus or fluid, telling the veterinarian that the mare has an infection that must be treated. Ovarian abnormalities and cysts are revealed on the ultrasound screen, as well as normal, single pregnancies and twins.

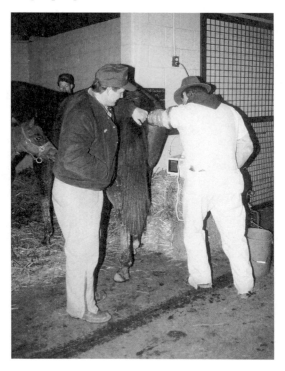

This mare is being examined by ultrasound. The rectal probe "reads" her organs and the picture is displayed on the monitor sitting on the bales.

(Photo courtesy of Martin Pierce)

Problem mares are the ones that benefit most from ultrasound. For example, a mare that was empty for two years should be examined with ultrasound in November. If the source of her problem is revealed, there is usually adequate time to treat her before the breeding season begins in February. Ultrasound is extremely helpful to the veterinarian who must piece together the puzzle of subfertility and solve a valuable mare's reproductive problems.

Uterine Biopsy: Less commonly employed is the uterine biopsy. Biopsies are usually performed in the fall on problem mares. Older mares, or mares with a history of problems conceiving or carrying foals to term, are candidates for a biopsy. Similar to the culture, the uterus is entered with a biopsy tool that snips a piece of the uterine lining. This is examined for infection, endometritis, gland problems or scar tissue. The results allow the veterinarian to determine the reason for the subfertility or to monitor the treatment of an infection.

Suturing Mares to Improve Reproductive Health: Suturing shut the external edges of the lips of the vulva, or Caslick's operation, is a simple, effective - yet the most overlooked - procedure that can be done to improve a mare's reproductive health. Mares are sutured to keep air, debris and fecal matter which cause irritation and infection from entering the vagina. An opening is left at the bottom for urination. Four or five weeks before foaling, the mare is opened up by the veterinarian.

Conformation usually dictates whether to suture a mare. Ideally, the vulva is vertical, with no tendency to slant or fall back under the anus. If a mare shows this good conformation with her external reproductive organs, that is, straight down under her tail, she may not need suturing. It's hard on her to be opened up from stem to stern every year. Mares with poor conformation of the external reproductive organs should always be sutured. If the operation is done once, the operation will need to be repeated every year in the future that she is bred.

Mares that suffer chronic infections are usually sutured as a part of the treatment for the infection. The medication is more effective in a sutured mare because recurring contamination and reinfection are eliminated. Even mares with "textbook perfect" conformation may suffer chronic infections. They must be sutured to regain their breeding soundness.

The procedure is often performed on racing fillies at the track because exercise at racing speed creates a negative pressure that sucks debris into the vagina. Suturing closed the vulva prevents this problem.

Often, young mares will gain weight during their first year off the racetrack. The fat gained around the pelvis and tail will support the vulva and may correct the need for this operation. It will be straight up and down as it should be. It probably won't be necessary to suture every mare you own, but do not overlook this simple procedure if it's indicated. It is preventative medicine of the best kind.

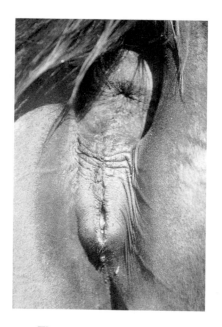 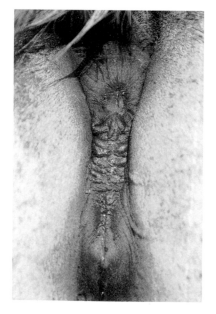

The mare on the left has a vulva that falls back under her tail. She is sutured to preserve her reproductive health. The mare on the right has good conformation but is sutured also.

(Photos courtesy of Martin Pierce)

Manipulating the Mare's Weight: In nature, mares are at their thinnest by the end of winter. As spring begins, they start to gain weight as the new grass appears. This is the time of greatest fertility in the horse. Our goal is to replicate this situation in the domesticated broodmare.

Manipulating mares' weight for greatest fertility begins in October. In the fall, all mares and fillies should be on a diet. Foaling mares are weaned from their foals and maintained without grain and the grain rations of barren mares are cut down or eliminated. Off-the-track fillies are let down slowly, preserving the lean condition they acquired on the racetrack. All these mares are brought down to a "subsistence" weight, to the point where you can see and feel the ribs. They are maintained in this condition through December.

On January 1st, the grain ration is slowly increased. The objective is to have the mare begin gaining 1/4 pound per day. Weigh the mare frequently to make certain you are achieving the proper results. When the mare reaches her normal weight, the increase in feed is leveled off. By this time, the well-managed mare is usually in foal.

By controlling the mare's weight so she is thin but gaining a quarter pound a day in the spring, we are mimicking nature. We are increasing our chances for conception.

Mare's Lights Program - Much of a successful breeding program depends upon a good Mare's Lights Program. John Gaines and I developed the first Mare's Lights Program for Thoroughbreds at Gainesway Farm.

John is an intelligent, creative man. If someone presents him with a good idea, he will consider it carefully. If he agrees that the idea has merit, he will provide the resources to promote it. In about 1963, John heard that Dr. John Patterson had begun using lights on mares at Hanover Shoe, one of the world's most prestigious Standardbred farms. John and I discussed the program with our veterinarian, Dr. Ed Fallon, and John decided that we would try it. Through some modifications, we arrived at our present Mare's Lights Program.

Simply put, the Mare's Lights Program means housing the mare under artificial light to mimic the long days of late spring and early summer. A 150-watt light bulb can fool her reproductive system into thinking it's May, her most fertile time, when it's only Valentine's Day. Anyone can put their mare under lights. Simply install a light in the stall which will deliver 300 footcandles (about a 150-watt bulb) to the mare. Have the light connected to a timer which turns on at 6 a.m. and which turns off at 10 p.m. The objective is to keep the mare under artificial or real light for a minimum of 16 hours a day, every day. Begin turning on the lights on December 1 and keep them on until about May 1, when the natural light is sufficiently intense. Every mare stays under the lights until the first part of May, even after she is bred. It's that simple.

The Mare's Lights Program cannot be used in a haphazard way if it is to be effective. The entire body of the mare must be continually bathed in light for the entire 16 hours. A large stall that lets the mare move out from under the lights and into the shadows defeats the purpose. If the mare is blanketed, the lights will not be effective. The mare must not be able to put her head outside the stall and avoid the light, even partially. Under lights means just what it says.

Although we were the first Thoroughbred farm to use lights, most good farms now do the same thing. The Mare's Lights Program has become one of the best reproductive tools that has ever been used. It saves covers, which saves the stallion and the mares, and it contributes to earlier births and a higher percentage of pregnancies.

The Mare's Heat Cycle: Mares are "seasonally polyestrous," meaning several periods of estrus or heat. These periods when mares are ready to breed and conceive occur at somewhat regular intervals of about 21 days. But these periods of receptiveness are seasonal - the natural breeding season is only from mid-spring to mid-summer. Effective use of the Mare's Lights Program pushes the natural season back a few months, allowing us to breed in February as though it were May.

Each heat period, the mare's system prepares for ovulation and possible fertilization. A substance called FSH, or Follicle Stimulating Hormone, causes a follicle to mature on the ovary; the rest of the reproductive system grows too, due to the influence of estrogen. These physical changes are felt and noted upon palpation.

As the mare comes close to being in heat, her behavior around male horses changes. This behavior is induced by exposing the mare to an amorous, yet docile male horse. The changes in the mare's attitude and posture are written down. A pattern emerges that helps the breeder know when to have the mare bred. This process is called "teasing." The records of her behavior are maintained on teasing charts. Teasing is an ancient - but invaluable - method of predicting heat in mares.

Actual estrus, or heat when the mare will accept the stallion, lasts for about five to seven days. Her readiness is shown by standing with her hind legs apart, urinating and "winking," which is the action of the vulva contracting and relaxing, and by accepting attention from the teaser. Toward the end of the five days, the follicle ruptures and the mare ovulates. If the stallion's sperm is present and the egg is fertilized, a pregnancy results. Otherwise, the mare's system enters a short period of adjustment, then begins its preparation for the next heat cycle.

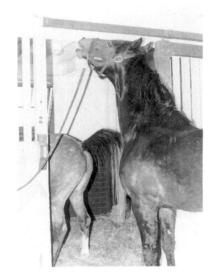

This mare shows she is in heat by being receptive to the teaser.
(Photo courtesy of Suzie Oldham)

The above description is vastly oversimplified. The actual mechanics of reproduction are quite complex and beyond the scope of this book. You need to understand only two important points: (1) Mares are delicate and highly unpredictable; the 21-day cycle is only an average and the cycles may or may not be regular; and, (2) you must employ qualified veterinarians and other personnel who understand the systems and individualistic nature of mares.

Synchronization: Synchronization means to manipulate mares' cycles to cause them to come into heat at specific, staggered intervals during the early months of spring. The veterinarian uses certain synthetic hormones to "prime" the mare's system, causing her to come into heat at a predictable point in time. Used in concert with the Mare's Lights

Program and weight manipulation, these hormones are a safe and effective way of getting more mares in foal earlier in the year.

Synchronization is an invaluable management tool for accommodating the large numbers of mares that are to be served during the breeding season. A stallion can only cover so many mares per day. If all mares came into heat on February 15th, only a fraction could be covered, while the remainder would have to wait until the next heat cycle. By synchronizing, or staggering the heat cycles, the mare manager and the stallion manager can arrange the available time to accommodate the majority of mares.

Timing the Cover: You will get more mares in foal with a single cover if the mare is bred just before she ovulates, rather than after she ovulates. There should be a reserve of viable sperm inside the mare waiting for the arrival of the egg.

Success in breeding racehorses depends upon the mare being covered at the proper relative time in her cycle, just before ovulation. I say relative because the time that a mare ovulates is not carved in stone. A mare's ovaries assume different characteristics at different times in her cycle, evident through palpation. The veterinarian notes these characteristics and their rate of change, and predicts a day when she will come into heat. At that time, she is examined again, and another prediction is made as to the approximate time of ovulation. Every effort is then made to have the mare in the breeding shed just before ovulation occurs. This precise, ideal timing saves the stallion's energy and saves the mare from the stress and possible contamination of multiple covers.

That is the way things are supposed to work. Unfortunately, two things can go wrong: predicting the time of ovulation can be a tricky business; and, if you guess wrong, the sperm may no longer be viable by the time the egg arrives. Some mares will deviate from their established patterns, or they may conceal their heats, making prediction a fine art. Others "hold" the ovulation until the night man falls asleep, or ovulate as the veterinarian is palpating them. It may be the stress of the artificial circumstances we impose on horses or it may be the simple contrariness of mares, but timing the cover is both a science and an art.

Consider the time and distance involved in getting the mare to the breeding shed and the fact that the mare's appointment with her intended mate is made days in advance. The stallion has many mares to service and each must "keep her appointment." Even though the mare may have been checked and monitored diligently, it is not always possible to have every mare at the breeding shed 90 minutes before ovulation.

To complicate matters further, the fertility of the stallion must be factored into the mare's timing. The sperm of every stallion has a definite life span of its own varying from a few hours to more than two days. Many breedings that "don't take" result from sperm that was no longer viable at the time the egg arrived. The sperm of all well-managed stallions is tested for life span and this information is available to you. A stallion's sperm that only lives for 12 or 18 hours demands particular precision from the veterinarian, the teasing man and the mare manager.

Breeding the Maiden Mare: Back before the Mare's Lights Program, people thought you shouldn't breed a maiden mare before Derby Day. They said that if you tried breeding her before that date, you would only get her dirty (infected) and you wouldn't get her in foal. And this was true. They wouldn't come into heat and the cervix wouldn't open. Now that we understand the needs of the maiden mare, we can coordinate the Mare's Lights Program and our stable management to convert maiden mares into pregnant mares early in the breeding season with only one cover. But it requires special effort and attention to accomplish this.

Maiden mares usually come off the racetrack in the fall. The maiden must be let down slowly, which means smoothing the transition from the racetrack to farm life. They are accustomed to daily exercise, regular grooming and warm stalls. It's a mistake to abruptly stop giving a maiden this kind of attention. The best housing for these maiden mares is in a box stall in the barn. Groom her every day, as she is accustomed.

Turn the mare outside by herself every day in a paddock (or in a round pen in bad weather) for exercise. In the beginning, she should only stay outside for about a half hour. In a few days, if she's quiet and comfortable, she may spend an hour outside. Then it's back into the barn. Each day she stays out a little longer, gradually extending the time until she's staying out all day. It is important that she come in before dark. If it's cold and rainy, she should come in early. Do not allow her become wet, cold or chilled.

Be cautious about introducing the maiden to the other mares. The maiden has not been turned out with other horses since she was a yearling. She is like the protected child, with no street smarts to help her avoid confrontations. If you turn her out for 10 or 12 hours a day with mares which bite and kick her, she will lose condition and she won't come into heat.

The veterinarian should spec, palpate and culture the maiden mare upon arrival at the farm. While the majority of maidens will have a clean culture, these tests should not be omitted. If she doesn't culture clean, now is the time to treat her until she comes up clean. If she was not sutured and if she needs to be, take care of this now.

As winter approaches, the maiden mare must be put on a diet. She must be losing a little weight. As she lets down, her hair coat will become dull. Beginning December 1, put her under lights. Keep her losing weight until January 1st, and then start increasing her feed. Watch her until you see the coat improve and she starts to gain weight. The coat will acquire good color and gloss and she may even shed some coat. She needs to gain about a quarter pound a day. Your eye isn't accurate enough to determine this - use a scale.

About 15 days after her feed is increased, she will have a "draggy heat." Keep track of this heat by observation and palpating, noting the duration and time of ovulation.

The process of coming to breeding readiness may take most of January or extend into February. You will see her condition improve steadily. By February 15th, the mare should be visibly heavier and shedding her winter coat. The "draggy heats" will become more intense and longer in duration. The mare that is gaining weight, condition and showing stronger heats is close to being ready to breed.

Start the countdown from the first good heat period. Schedule the cover for the second good heat. With the proper preparation, the first good heat is in early January or even late December. Under good management, chances are that the properly prepared mare will

174

experience her second strong heat about mid-February, right on schedule. If the first good heat is February 10th, wait and breed her on the next one, which would be around the first of March. The mare that came off the track on October 1st can be bred in February or March along with the other broodmares.

Maiden mares that arrive from the racetrack in March, April or May must be examined and cultured for breeding soundness as soon as possible. Have them teased right after they arrive. It's possible that these mares are ready to be bred in the first week they arrive, so tease the mare and get your culture results in 24 hours. You must act quickly or lose the opportunity to breed these late arrivals in this breeding season.

Whether you breed these maidens in the first week or eight weeks later will depend on the individual mare's cycle and the quality of the management she receives. Be certain to give them the same attention received by the mares arriving in October. The treatment should be similar to what they received at the racetrack. Keep them gaining weight and avoid stressing them. Neglect these mares and they will go "backwards" and lose condition. They may not cycle at all during the breeding season. You could lose the chance to breed and get a foal out of them next spring.

Maiden Mare Syndrome: The condition known as *maiden mare syndrome* is usually associated with fillies that have just come off the racetrack. The term suggests a condition or disease that afflicts maiden mares and must be "cured." Difficult, witchy behavior and failure to accept the stallion or to conceive are attributed to the syndrome.

The truth is that these mares' systems are simply not accustomed to the routines of the farm. This is more than a matter of attitude. The demands of racetrack training are such that the horse is brought to its peak of fitness. All her systems are tuned toward producing an ultimate effort on the track. Extra body weight is trained off the mare - she is an athlete, not a mother. Under such stress, non-essential systems will shut down temporarily. "Reproduction is a luxury," my veterinarian says. Your goal is to get the maiden's systems back to the normal, unstressed state where she can afford this luxury.

Keep in mind that the maiden mare has not been turned out in company since foalhood. She might be intimidated by the other mares and not know how to avoid being bullied. Similarly, the attentions of the teaser are foreign to her. Kicking and other bad behavior are merely acts of self defense.

Avoiding the onset of maiden mare syndrome is the test of your horsemanship. The maiden mare must be treated gently and with patience. To some extent, she must be pampered. In some cases, she must be taught new lessons. If she is handled with patience, if she is not bitten or treated roughly by the teaser, she will relax and begin to cycle and show heat normally.

Having the Maiden Mare Jumped: An important part of the maiden's education is being "jumped." This means having the teaser or a special jump horse wearing a shield mount her so she becomes accustomed to the experience. A maiden mare that has never had a horse mount her until she reaches the breeding shed is naturally going to become frightened and will misbehave. Do not send your maidens off to the stallion until they have had this experience. You are risking the handlers' safety, your mare's well-being and your reputation when you send a mare that has never been jumped. Since your goal is to cover this maiden mare only once, you increase your chances for success by making sure that she has had this experience.

Maiden Mares on Steroids: Some mares coming off the racetrack were given steroids while in training. Such medications can have hormonal and behavioral side effects. The ovaries of the mare may not cycle properly for breeding and her temperament is often too aggressive to allow her to be bred. These mares need time, perhaps as long as two months, for the effects of the drug to wear off. There is nothing you can do to speed up this process. It must simply wear off. However, you may look forward to the mare's temperament improving while you wait.

176

Barren Mares: "Barren" simply means that a mare is "empty" or not carrying a foal. The most comforting reason for a mare being barren is that she wasn't covered last year. Mares that are barren because they were not covered the previous year are handled the same as the maidens. Such mares should be examined and cultured in July or August. This will prevent an unpleasant surprise in November or December.

A barren mare that was covered last season is a different story. If the mare didn't conceive after breeding, you need to know several things. How many times was she covered? How accurate were her previous teasing charts? Is there a fertility problem with the stallion? And, most important, what does a complete examination for breeding soundness reveal? This is a situation where the veterinarian will need to do a whole battery of diagnostic tests. If there is an infection, it must be treated and she must be cultured again, repeating the process until the culture is clean. Allow several months to accomplish this, because certain infections are stubborn and may require several courses of treatment.

The battery of tests may reveal more serious problems that prevent the mare from conceiving and carrying a foal to term. A mare that is pooling urine in her vagina is a poor risk. Or the mare may have suffered so many untreated infections that her uterus is no longer able to nourish and maintain a pregnancy. If your mare has either of these problems, she will need one of two things: (1) A sizeable investment in veterinary services and patience to get her in foal one more time; or (2) a new owner.

There may be other reasons why the barren mare hasn't conceived. Perhaps she doesn't show her heats well. You might try to tease her in the morning and she'll have no part of it, even though the calendar says she's ready. Now, it's busy in the morning, lots of activity, and that mare is feeling a little timid and she's not going to show anything. She's in heat, but she won't tell you when you ask her. You have to work with her. Watch her when she is out with the other mares. Put her next to another mare that's being teased. Visit her in the evening when it's quiet. Watch her when she's relaxed and not under any pressure and she may tell you what you need to know.

Maybe the barren mare has had a bad experience. She might have been pinned down and twitched for the teaser when she wasn't ready. She may have been covered before or after the time she was ready and suffered some bruising. Six or seven hours can make a big difference to a mare. Breed her when she isn't ready, treat her roughly or hurt her and you've created a problem. You'll have to work carefully to overcome that bad experience.

Try to keep the barren mare calm and happy. Be sure that she gets along with the other mares you have housed next to her. It may help to stable her next to different mares until you find one with which she is content. You may have to experiment to find what will please her. Wherever you see her calm down or her attitude improve, keep her there. Some mares are happier in certain stalls and anything which makes a mare more content increases your chances of getting her in foal.

A mare that is barren because she aborted her foal is always a special risk. There is always the possibility that she will lose the next foal, so do some detective work. Did she miss her vaccinations? Was she stressed unduly by shipping or a change in environment? If it's possible to determine why she aborted, you can take steps to prevent it from happening again.

Here again, a veterinary examination may disclose the reason for the abortion. The mare may have had a tear in the vagina or cervix, or poor tone to the cervix. A cervix that has been sutured several times is not the muscular structure it originally was. It is now mainly scar tissue which fails to form a tight seal and may cause the mare to abort. The condition may not prevent her from getting in foal, but she will not carry the pregnancy successfully to term. This mare might need a new owner, too. Your veterinarian can advise you as to the chances for a successful repair.

It is particularly important to get the whole story on a barren mare's condition. If you ignore her health, she may show a heat, and she may accept the stallion, but she won't produce a foal for you. It's crucial to have her in the best reproductive health.

Foaling Mares: The mare that had a foal last year but failed to conceive this season must be monitored carefully. There is usually a good reason that she didn't conceive and the problem must be diagnosed and treated. Culture her in August, before her present foal is weaned. She may have a stubborn infection that will require several courses of treatment. She may need to be sutured if she's taking in debris or manure. Do not wait until November to investigate her subfertility. The longer she is infected, the more damage she may incur. To insure her reproductive soundness and to stay on schedule, she should have two clean cultures back-to-back by December .

A mare may pick up extra weight while on pasture with her foal. She should start losing weight after weaning. Put her out on extremely short grass, almost a bare lot. Throw her a flake of hay, but nothing else. She should continue losing weight until January 1. Look for her ribs. Don't let her start gaining until January 1. Then start her on a little grain and let her start gaining a quarter pound per day. Use your scale.

During this time, chart her heats and watch her behavior and condition. If she cultures clean in mid-December, plan on breeding her in mid-February. She'll probably get right in foal.

Failure to Accept the Stallion: Occasionally, will you find a mare that is barren because she refuses to accept the stallion or because she has other behavioral problems. Some are difficult, even dangerous to breed.

Foaling mares should always be handled with caution, so they aren't unduly stressed and so they don't injure anyone. Concerned about her foal at home, a mare will sometimes kick without warning or reason.

A few mares will kick and refuse to accept any horse and make dealing with them hazardous. Other mares will break down and show their interest only when they get to the breeding shed and see the stallion himself, rejecting the teaser every time. The best policy is to keep trying for the right moment, within a few hours of ovulation when most of them will break down and accept the teaser and the stallion.

I cannot emphasize too strongly that the mare must be physiologically ready for breeding. If the results of her palpation and spec exam are not consistent with the signs of a good heat, she is not ready. She must have a big follicle and the cervix must be relaxed or expect her behavior to be terrible because she's not ready. A very few mares will have all the signs of a good, strong heat and still won't accept the stallion. For the safety of the handlers and the stallion, these few remaining hold-outs may need to be tranquilized.

Overweight Mares: An overweight mare is a problem. A mare that's too fat won't conceive easily. Be certain she's getting proper exercise, even if this means working her in the round pen every other day. If she's eating the other mares' rations, she may need to be brought inside at feeding time. She must be thin at the start of breeding season and gaining slowly, about a quarter pound per day. The mare's ribs should be barely visible but easily felt. Thin but gaining is the best condition for conception.

Foal Heat: Somewhere between 7 and 15 days after foaling, the mare will come into heat. This is called the *foal heat.* When we talk about broodmares, the question of breeding on the foal heat always comes up. Should you or shouldn't you breed back on the foal heat?

The most compelling reason for breeding a mare during foal heat is to get an earlier foal next year. Breeding on the foal heat will move up the date of next year's foal by about 20 days. Breeding on the heat following foal heat will give you a foal on about the same date as this year.

A second reason to breed on the foal heat concerns difficult mares. Mares that don't show their heats well or have few good, strong heats are candidates to be bred back right away. The foal heat is the most predictable of all heats, making this the best time for an unpredictable mare to be bred.

The decision to breed on foal heat is completely dependent on the health of the mare. If she has any problems such as an infection, bruising, tearing or even an off-color to the cervix, don't breed her. She won't get in foal. It will only delay the healing. Let that heat pass and breed her on the next one, 28 to 32 days after foaling. By then she has had time to heal. She'll probably catch and she'll foal about the same date next year as this year.

As a rule of thumb, I don't consider breeding on foal heat until the first part of April. Prior to that, I wait for the second heat. The reason is that mares in Kentucky don't get outside enough with their young foals in early spring. They don't get the proper exercise, so their systems are not perfectly ready for reproduction.

By mid-April or early May, I begin to take a hard look at foaling mares to see if they can be bred on the foal heat. If she has a normal heat and is in good shape physically (no bruising, good color), I won't hesitate to breed her. If everything goes well, this is the time I can move up her production schedule.

There are two exceptions to the before/after April foal heat policy. A few mares won't come into foal heat until 13 to 16 days after foaling. This extra time allows them to heal and recover from foaling. Such a mare is ahead of the nine-day mare in condition and, if the veterinarian finds her perfectly healthy for breeding, you have a good shot at getting her in foal, regardless of the calendar.

The big exception is the mare that comes into heat seven days after foaling. Never breed on a seven-day foal heat, regardless of how perfect the mare's condition or how late in the year. Seven days is not enough time for the mare to recover from foaling. Usually, she will not get in foal and you will only delay her healing and her production schedule by stressing her and getting her dirty.

Double Breeding: Double breeding means having the stallion cover the mare more than once during one heat period. Some mare owners insist that their mare be double bred. They believe that a double breeding will increase the chances of conception. Most of the time they are not helping themselves at all and are risking the first, good cover.

Consider the following situation: The mare has been bred. She showed a good, strong heat and accepted the stallion. You know it was a good cover. You may be tempted to "double up" and cover her again, but don't do it. If you do, you are only asking for trouble. If the second cover occurs after the mare has ovulated, she'll fight. She'll be mad and she can become torn or bruised from moving around. She may even get infected. She may kick the stallion because she doesn't want anything to do with him. It's going against nature to try and breed that mare after she has ovulated.

One situation that calls for a double breeding is when the stallion's sperm are not long-lived, and the mare has not yet ovulated within the life span of the sperm. A good stallion manager will know his horse's fertility. If the stallion's sperm live for 48 hours and the mare ovulates 12 hours after the cover, it's useless to cover her again. But if the sperm are not viable after thirty hours and the mare was covered thirty six hours ago and has yet to ovulate, it might be necessary to double up. Some top stallion managers can read a mare's body language and know if the mare should be covered again. If you're lucky enough to deal with such an individual, and I can only think of two such men, respect his judgment.

The smart thing to do is to have the mare palpated after the cover to determine if she has ovulated within the life span of the stallion's sperm. Be sure to use the same veterinarian who palpated her before the first cover. A different veterinarian might not be able to tell if she has ovulated. The same veterinarian will know if it makes sense to double up on her.

Another situation that calls for a double breeding is if the stallion fails to ejaculate. This may occur as the result of a distraction to the horse or it can be a characteristic of a particular stallion. Whatever the reason, the stallion handler will check for this and if the horse did not ejaculate, the mare needs to be covered again immediately.

Monitoring the Pregnant Mare: The mare should be examined by the veterinarian 16 to 18 days after breeding. The veterinarian will palpate the mare to feel the tone of her tissues and organs, then do an ultrasound to corroborate those findings. If the palpation and the ultrasound findings contradict each other or he suspects a problem, he may want to run a blood test.

The ultrasound will tell the veterinarian one of several things. He will find: (1) a normal, pregnant mare with a single pregnancy, which is what we are hoping to find; (2) a normal, non-pregnant mare; (3) edema, which is a non-pregnant mare coming back into heat; (4) twins; or (5) fluid in the uterus, which is pus and signals an infection.

If all checks out, the normal, pregnant mare will be palpated and examined with ultrasound again at 25 to 28 days. Palpation exams follow at 35 days, again at 45 days and at 60 days and finally at 90 to 120 days.

The chart below gives you a schedule for arranging examinations with your veterinarian. It is not all-inclusive, but will give you an idea of what the veterinarian is looking for at each stage. Certain problems, such as mares carrying twin embryos, may need more frequent palpations and/or ultrasounds. Your veterinarian will guide you.

Monitoring Pregnant Mares	
Days after breeding	**Procedures**
16 to 18 days	Palpation and Ultrasound - checking for pregnancy, twins, problems.
25 to 28 days	Palpation and Ultrasound - follow-up for absence of twins, checking for fetal viability.
35 days	Palpation - check for good bulge and tone.
45 days	Palpation - time of placentation, check for fetal size and normal tone.
60 days	Palpation - check for fetal size and development.
90 to 120 days	Palpation - to confirm pregnancy.

Twins: Many animals produce healthy twin offspring. This is not the case in horses. Approximately 3% of all Thoroughbred and Standardbred pregnancies are twin pregnancies and each one is a potential tragedy. Twin foal fetuses must compete for limited space and nourishment. One twin usually dies and, if this occurs late in the pregnancy, the other fetus is jeopardized by the presence of the dead twin. The surviving twin is usually weak and at risk. Rarely do either survive the entire term and if they do, the mare is imperiled. All you need to know is the time-worn phrase, "Twins are a disaster."

During the first ultrasound exam the veterinarian will check for twins. Don't wait until later. At this stage, the veterinarian can pinch off one twin with the least danger to the other. If you wait longer, the process will cause inflammation and neither embryo may survive.

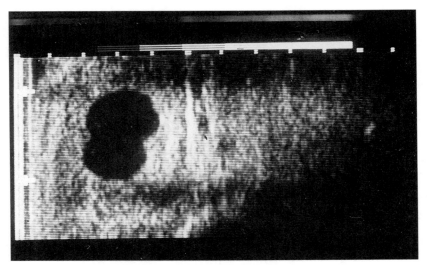

Photo of ultrasound showing twin embryos of 14 and 15 days.
(Photo courtesy of O. J. Ginther, University of Wisconsin)

The veterinarian will want to check the mare again two to four days later to make certain that there is only one embryo. If this second check is good, the mare goes back on the normal schedule of exams. If the single pregnancy is still there at 42 days, you have an insurable pregnancy. She's in foal and now you have to keep her that way.

Maintaining the Pregnancy by Eliminating Stress: Stress is the greatest enemy of the developing fetus. In my opinion, stress causes more abortions than any other factor. The formula for maintaining a healthy, pregnant mare is simple: Keep her calm and content. Keep the pregnant mare healthy, which makes her feel good, and change as little as possible in her daily routine, which makes her happy. Horses, being creatures of habit and lovers of routine, will thrive in a quiet, orderly environment where change occurs slowly, if at all.

Transporting Pregnant Mares: One of the greatest stresses imposed on a pregnant mare is to put her on a van and transport her a long distance. My rule of thumb is to have a mare 60 days in foal to travel 50 miles and 100 days in foal to travel more than 50 miles. Putting her on a van from Kentucky to Florida at 40 days is commonly followed by a phone call saying she's no longer in foal.

You may observe a fellow breeder take his mare home before she's 50 days into the pregnancy. There is a strong possibility that he will get her home safely, only to find two weeks later that she has either aborted the fetus or has absorbed it. The unfortunate mare owner may wonder if she was in foal in the first place. The mare manager and veterinarian can verify the pregnancy from the ultrasound picture, but their carefully orchestrated teamwork is wasted because of a hasty move. The mare is now barren and the cause is stress.

Hoof Care: Care of the feet is an area of broodmare management which is frequently neglected. You see chipped feet, overgrown feet and mares that are footsore because they aren't shod but should have been. Pain in a mare's feet can cause her to lose condition. This is simple neglect and causes stress to the mare.

Pregnant mares need to be trimmed every 30 days. The farrier should round off the wall, leaving plenty of sole. I prefer to keep mares barefoot, but a mare that has thin walls or tender soles must be kept shod. If you plan to pull a mare's shoes and let her go barefoot, wait for damp weather when the ground is soft. Rub some *Corona*™ or other hoof ointment into the coronary band, which will keep the feet pliable and encourage growth. She must be kept comfortable.

Weaning the Foal from the Mare: Most horsemen establish weaning practices based upon what they believe is in the best interest of the foal. They assume the mare will adjust to whatever stresses weaning imposes on her. This is a mistake. Weaning causes more stress to the mare than it does to the foal.

A common practice is to wean the foal when the mare is 90 days pregnant. By then the foal is about four months old and eating enough grass and grain to do without the milk. No matter at what age you wean, the mare is going to run and get excited and be upset for days. This stress so early in the pregnancy, in my opinion, is a common cause for mares to abort their fetuses. I'd rather wean when the mare is five to six months into her pregnancy. By the sixth month, the mare isn't making much milk anymore. Her foal is somewhat independent and probably has nursed from mares other than its dam. Weaning at this stage is much less stressful to the mare. The further along she is, the safer you are.

Allow some flexibility in weaning. Do not wean immediately after vaccinations, a traumatic session with the farrier or any other event that causes stress to the mare or foal. If the weather turns unseasonably harsh or if the mare and foal are adjusting to a new pasture mate, postpone the weaning until both horses have had several days to adjust. This may seem unnecessarily cautious, but think of this as "health insurance" for the foal, the mare and the fetus she carries.

Other Sources of Stress: Stress to pregnant mares doesn't come only from shipping, sore feet or weaning. It can result from illness, lameness or from changing the mare's feed, pasture or companions. If you must change some aspect of a mare's environment, do it cautiously. Watch her carefully for signs of nervousness or agitation. Minimize the risk to your investment by keeping the pregnant mare in a serene state of mind, as nature intended.

Don't move the mare to a new barn. Don't put her out with a new group of mares where she'll be chased around the field. Keep her with a group of five or six other mares that get along with her. A change of companions means re-establishing the pecking order and this means stress.

As the weather improves, she'll be out longer and longer. Her weight will come up where you want it. Don't let her get too fat.

That's more stress on her. Keep her in good flesh, with her ribs covered but not buried.

Continue to feed the newly pregnant mare so she's gaining a quarter pound a day. Keep her under the lights through her 100th day or until the natural light catches up. Keep doing the same things that she's accustomed to so you don't stress her.

Progesterone Therapy: Progesterone is the hormone of pregnancy. The mare needs a continuous, high level of this hormone to remain safely in foal. Those mares that fail to produce adequate amounts of this hormone to remain pregnant are often successfully treated with some type of progesterone therapy. There are several forms available, such as progesterone in oil, injectable progesterone and its synthetic form, Regumate™.

A mare with a history of losing early pregnancies needs a blood test five days after ovulation to determine if her ovaries are producing sufficient progesterone. If the blood test indicates a problem, the veterinarian may prescribe some form of progesterone therapy. The mare will need another blood test at 12 days to check on the effectiveness of this therapy, another at 21 days and, if deemed necessary by the veterinarian, another at 30 or 36 days to make sure that her progesterone levels are within safe limits.

Regumate™ is a synthetic form of progesterone, commonly used in mares that have sustained some damage to the cervix or from a laceration during birth or breeding. Such damage prevents the cervix from having good tone and maintaining the seal. Regumate™ is helpful in maintaining the tone of the cervix.

Other forms of progesterone are used to offset the stressful effects of an injury, a lameness such as laminitis or of transporting a mare long distance. The right hormonal therapy is quite effective in regulating the hormonal fluctuations that can occur in these unusual situations.

Preparing the Mare for Foaling: During the last two to three months of pregnancy, the fetus significantly increases its demands on the mare's systems. This is when the fetus develops most of its size and mares which appeared sleek and trim for months suddenly grow large with foal. The mare's appetite will increase to meet the growing demands. Special feeding and management routines are required to meet her needs.

Feeding the Pre-foaling Mare: Mares receive no grain for the 10 days following weaning, then are gradually brought up to a subsistence level of grain. They are brought through the winter in a slightly lean condition, then are brought up in weight as early spring approaches. A mare that is an easy keeper can get along on three to five pounds of grain once a day. An average mare probably eats about seven pounds a day. Mares eat their grain outside in all but the worst weather.

Sixty to 90 days before foaling, the mare's grain is increased to meet her increased nutritional requirements. How much to increase the grain depends upon the individual mare. She should be brought into the barn for feeding each morning and evening, effectively doubling the amount of grain. Most mares will need about 14 pounds of grain (seven pounds fed twice a day) for this period before foaling. As always, you feed to condition, keeping the mare's ribs covered but not buried in flesh. Easy keepers may wait until 60 days prior to foaling for the increase in grain, while leaner mares need an increase in feed at 90 days. If she stocks up - showing edema, which is a fluid filling in the lower legs that disappears with exercise - cut back on her grain. Otherwise maintain the 14 pounds a day. If the weather is good, turn these mares outside again after eating.

This is a good time to evaluate the quality of your facilities and investigate the accessibility of good veterinary help in your area. If the mare's stall is large, safe and clean, and a good veterinarian is only 15 minutes away, excellent. But if you live in an area where the closest equine specialist is an hour away, you may have a problem. In such a case, you may want to consider sending the mare to a farm specializing in foaling, where there are good facilities and qualified veterinarians and staff. If the mare must be shipped a long distance to be bred back, you may as well send her off 90 days before foaling. This will cost a little extra in board bills, but measured against losing a valuable foal or mare, it is cheap insurance.

Nightwatch: The mare must be brought inside at night 30 to 45 days prior to foaling for nightwatch. Mares with a history of foaling two or three weeks early are brought in for nightwatch before the 45-day mark.

Bring the mare in at about 4:00 p.m. and turn her out the next morning at 7:00 a.m. The person in charge of the nightwatch must know how to inspect the udders as he checks the mares. The mare's udder is capable of making drastic changes in a short period of time - it may be the only indication that the mare is going to surprise you by foaling early.

Vaccinations: Sixty to 90 days prior to foaling is the time to review the mare's worming and vaccination records. Her shots must be current a month before foaling for the production of antibody-rich colostrum. The complete schedule of vaccinations and worming appears in the chapter, *General Farm Routine*. Read it and consult your veterinarian for the vaccination schedule appropriate to your area of the country.

Colostrum: Sometimes a mare does not produce sufficient milk for her foal. Other times, the delivery is so difficult that she is unable to stand so her foal can nurse. And, tragically, the mare may die during foaling. An important part of preparing for foaling is the collection of colostrum.

Colostrum is the first milk produced by the mare. It is rich with antibodies that the newborn foal needs to survive. If the foal doesn't receive a pint or so of this first milk within the first 15 hours or so, his immune system may not function properly. The foal begins to lose his capacity to benefit from colostrum about 15 hours after birth. This capacity continues to wane and by the end of the first 24 hours, the foal is at great risk of becoming sick and dying if he has not had colostrum.

Start collecting a little colostrum from the older mares shortly before or after their foals nurse so you are prepared for an emergency. Maiden mares are not good colostrum donors - collect from the mares with histories of producing adequate amounts of good quality colostrum. Collect from any mare that is leaking or losing her colostrum.

Colostrum is collected by milking the mare with the index finger and thumb. The squeeze and pull action is similar to milking a cow, but tact and gentleness are important if you hope to avoid being kicked. Use sterile containers for collection, label and date the containers and freeze them. Keep collecting and replenishing your supply as needed. If you're only expecting two foals, a pint or two is sufficient. If you don't have enough mares to maintain a supply, locate a colostrum bank through your veterinarian or a fellow breeder, or line up a nurse mare.

Nurse Mares: Every breeder must know where he can get a nurse mare on short notice. If a mare dies during foaling or is injured too severely to stand for nursing, or if she does not produce enough milk, another provider of mare's milk must be obtained quickly.

Nurse mares are generally grade mares that foal each year. In Kentucky, some farms breed and maintain nurse mares exclusively for the purpose of serving as foster mothers. Qualifications for a good nurse mare are a tolerant attitude and the ability to produce quality milk. The usual arrangement is to lease a nurse mare for a specific length of time.

As the need arises, labor is induced in a nurse mare that is close to foaling. When the nurse mare's foal is born, it is taken away and your newborn foal is substituted. If your foal is orphaned at three and a half weeks of age, a nurse mare with a foal of about the same age is selected. Success in using nurse mares depends on your foal and the nurse mare's foal being the same age. This compatibility in foal ages encourages the nurse mare to accept your foal.

What happens to the foals of the nurse mares? Some of the foals are bottle-fed, then donated to universities for research, but many more are given away for 4-H projects. I know some nurse mare farms that have a waiting list of people who want to adopt these foals.

If your mare should die or become too ill to nurse, you will need a nurse mare. Don't wait until disaster strikes to find out how to obtain one.

Test for Jaundice: At 30 days prior to foaling, test the mare's blood for "jaundice," or isohemolytic icterus, which is the incompatibility between the antibodies in the mare's colostrum and the foal's red blood cells. This occurs when the foal inherits certain types of red blood cells from the stallion. Roughly comparable to Rh factor in human babies, this condition is deadly if not detected in time. If this incompatibility between the red blood cells of the foal and the colostrum of the mare exists, the foal will die from nursing on the colostrum.

Fortunately, the simple "jaundice" blood test will predict this condition. If necessary, steps can be taken to obtain compatible colostrum - which has been tested - from a colostrum bank. The foal must be muzzled or prevented from nursing from his dam. After the mare is no longer producing colostrum or the foal is more than 15 hours old, the foal is allowed to nurse again.

Remove Sutures: Thirty days before foaling is the time to open up the mare if she is stitched. Do not fail to do this. Failing to open a stitched mare before foaling is the grossest sort of neglect. This simple procedure also provides the veterinarian with another opportunity to look at the mare before foaling and assess her condition.

Preparing a Place for the Mare to Foal: Most mares foal at night. Probably 75% of all mares give birth between 10:00 p.m. and 6:00 a.m. while they are in the barn. However, you may see a mare showing signs of foaling in the daytime while she's turned out. If she's out alone in a clean paddock and the weather is mild, leave her there. This is the ideal place for her to foal. It is stressful to the mare to be moved inside at this point. A clear area of grass that the sun has washed is cleaner than your foaling stall. If your mare has chosen to foal outside and there are no hazards in the weather or environment, let her stay where she is comfortable. This is as nature intended and is the most desirable situation.

The use of a special foaling stall, while once the absolute rule, has fallen off somewhat in recent years. The average-sized stall on most farms is 12 ft. X 14 ft. - plenty large for foaling. The mare is more comfortable in her own familiar stall. She has been exposed to its inevitable germs and has developed immunities to most of them. The foaling stall, no matter how thoroughly scrubbed, will present a challenge to her in the form of new bacteria and viruses. Unless the weather is extremely cold, well below freezing, leave the mare in her own stall to foal. This practice has shown to cut down on disease.

If problems are expected or encountered or if the mare is due to foal during extremely cold weather, use your foaling stall. At least two weeks before the mare is due, disinfect the floors and walls and bed the stall thickly with straw. If it's mid-winter, have a heat lamp handy.

If the mare has never been in the foaling stall and is brought in as her labor starts, she may become agitated and delay the progress of the labor. This is stressful to the mare and can be avoided with preparation. During the last 30 days, take the mare into the foaling stall so she can become comfortable in it. If she is restless, take her out after a few minutes. Try again in a day or two. Give her the opportunity to relax, eat a meal and nap in it.

The Medicine Chest: Every foaling barn needs a medicine cabinet within view of the foaling stall. There should be a sink nearby for washing. A double stainless steel sink works well. Keep one side reserved for sterile work.

Keep these items on hand: rubber gloves, bandages, sterile cotton, alcohol, iodine, a jigger, surgical scissors, needles and syringes of all sizes, Banamine, Combiotic or another broad-spectrum antibiotic, a thermometer, tail wraps, a lubricant like K-Y jelly, soaps, towels and disinfectants, foaling or OB straps, an enema already prepared and ingredients for more, a scale for weighing the afterbirth, oxygen and a special bag and mask called an Ambu bag to administer the oxygen.

Many of these items will be available at any pharmacy. Others you will need to get from your veterinarian. He will explain their uses to you. The period immediately after foaling is the period of highest mortality in foals, so be prepared.

Most of the problems associated with foaling are preventable with careful planning and preparation in the weeks beforehand. Have your medicine cabinet ready, the freezer stocked with colostrum, and a nurse mare lined up in case you need her. Have the veterinarian's phone numbers written down by the phone. Discuss your preparations with him ahead of time. Know how to get a horse van to your property on a moment's notice. Chances are, your mare will foal without incident. But if she has trouble, these precautions will save time and may save the lives of your mare and foal.

Monitoring: As the mare's time approaches, she must be closely monitored. By closely monitored, I mean every five to 10 minutes. When she begins to paw, circle and sweat, the night man should alert the foaling man. A mare with a history of difficult deliveries or a mare showing signs of having a problem warrants a call to the veterinarian at this time.

A horse van parked outside and ready to go can save the lives of mares and foals in the event of trouble. A competent veterinary hospital can perform a Caesarean section if necessary, but this operation is rarely successful if done on the farm due to unsterile conditions. While 95% of foalings proceed without incident, some bad presentations, meaning the foal is not lined up correctly to pass through the birth canal, can only be saved by a C-section.

Chapter 10

Foal Management

Good foal management begins in the hours and minutes before your foal enters this world. There are no actions you can take, no decisions you can make that are more important in the life of your new horse than those immediately before and after foaling.

Foaling: Predicting the time of foaling can be difficult. Maiden mares are notoriously unpredictable in their preparations for foaling.

Mares may signal their readiness to foal in several ways. The udder develops and fills, first with a clear liquid and then with milk. The teats will "wax" or show an accumulation of a sticky substance. This waxing is a signal that birth is hours or a day away. The muscles around the croup and tail may become soft and slack and the vulva may appear longer as the ligaments relax. All or none of these signs may be present.

Labor is usually described in three stages: (1) Minor contractions, up to the point when the water breaks; (2) actual delivery, which begins as the water breaks; and, (3) expulsion of the afterbirth.

The first stage of labor varies greatly from mare to mare. Some mares circle, lay down, get up, sweat, paw and are restless for hours. Others show these signs intermittently for several hours, or only exhibit this behavior for a few minutes before actual delivery. Restlessness is not usually a danger signal. The mare may lay down and get up repeatedly to shift the foal into the proper position for delivery. Every mare is different. If the mare has produced a foal before, her past behavior is the best indication of what to expect from her.

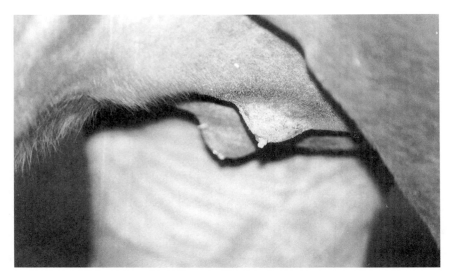

**The mare's udder that is full of milk and shows "wax" on the ends
of the teats is a good - but not infallible- indicator that she will foal
in the next day or so.** *(Photo courtesy of Martin Pierce)*

The second stage of labor, the delivery, begins when the cervix opens and the water breaks. This "water" is allantoic fluid, which appears as a great gush of pale liquid from the vulva. At this point most mares - not all - will lay down to deliver their foals. Some don't use good judgment in choosing a place to foal. If the foaling man sees the mare laying with her hindquarters backed up to the wall or the door, he and his assistant must help reposition her. Those few mares that try to deliver standing up should be encouraged to lay down. It may help to lead the mare in small half-circles in the center of the stall. The mare might be afraid - try leaving the stall for a few moments to give her a chance to lay down. If no one can coax the mare to lay down, an assistant must be ready to catch the foal.

The Normal Delivery: Normal delivery is a short, explosive process. Most mares deliver their foals about twenty minutes after the water breaks. Foals are born front feet first, in an upright position with the head laying across the front legs. Picture the newborn diving out of his dam, one front foot slightly ahead of the other so the shoulders can slip through.

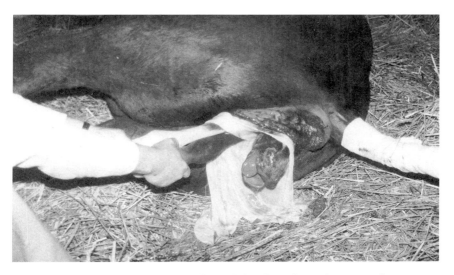

This foal is presented normally with forelegs first, then muzzle. The foaling man is grasping the forelegs to help the mare as she pushes the foal's shoulders through the pelvic opening.

(Photo courtesy of Martin Pierce)

An experienced foaling man should examine the mare early in her labor to determine that the forelegs and head are being presented properly. Sometimes a foal's elbow will lock or catch against the mare's pelvis. The foaling man knows how to reach his scrubbed arm into the mare and unlock the elbow. When the shoulders are out, the mare may pause to rest for a moment, perhaps 30 seconds. When she resumes pushing, the foaling man may "pull" the foal gently downwards towards the mare's hocks in time with the contractions. "Pull" does not mean to haul or use force. The foaling man simply holds the progress the mare has made with her pushing efforts, assisting the passage of the foal's hips through the birth canal.

As soon as the foal is out the birth canal, break the membranous sac around its nostrils and wipe them clean. Make sure the foal is breathing comfortably on his own. If the foal is having

197

trouble breathing, you must give artificial respiration. Ideally, this is combined with oxygen. Serious problems can develop if the foal is deprived of oxygen during birth. A weak foal or one which required artificial respiration may need an additional source of oxygen for a period of time. Check with your veterinarian for ways to prepare for this problem. If he recommends an artificial source of oxygen, learn how to use it before the foaling season. If a means of supplying oxygen is not available, give artificial respiration by blowing into the foal's nostrils.

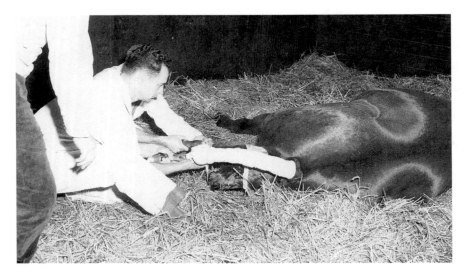

The foaling man may assist the mare's efforts by directing the foal toward the mare's hocks, helping the foal to slip over the pelvic opening and out the birth canal.

(Photo courtesy of J. C. Skeets Meadors)

When the foal is breathing well on his own, let him lie quietly in the straw for about five minutes still attached to the mare by the umbilical cord. You may see the blood pulsating through the cord. As long as blood flows through the cord, the foal should continue to receive that blood from the mare. This flow of blood tapers off rapidly, usually within five minutes, but those few extra minutes on his dam's system give the foal extra strength and allow the mare to rest.

Don't rush in to break the umbilical cord. Give them a few, uninterrupted minutes.

Often, the mare gets to her feet soon after foaling. In doing so, she places tension on the cord and it breaks naturally. If it doesn't, break it with your fingers. There is a spot about an inch from the foal's stomach where the cord is like the coupling on a hose. This spot turns white as the blood flowing through the umbilical cord tapers off. It will feel like a piece of gristle around the cord. This is the spot where the cord will break naturally and is the only spot where you should break it manually.

Don't rip the cord from the foal's belly. Grasp the cord with one hand on each side of the coupling. Because this coupling is only an inch or so away from the foal, one hand will be touching the foal's belly. The thumb and forefinger of this hand should grasp the cord firmly while the palm or the heel of the hand rests on the foal's belly. Break the cord either by rubbing the gristle-like coupling over your knuckle or with a short, quick pull. To pull the cord apart, one hand must steady the cord's attachment to the foal. This hand remains absolutely still to prevent the cord from being ripped from the foal's belly. The other hand is the pulling hand. It grasps the cord on the mare's side of the coupling and makes a quick pull *leading toward the mare but not against the foal.* Don't cut the cord with a scissors. It should break naturally, leaving rough edges that help seal the ends. The ends of the cord normally bleed a little. The blood washes out any bacteria.

Disinfect the naval stump immediately after the cord is broken. The easiest way is to pour iodine into a jigger. The large end holds 1 1/2 ounces. Put it up to the stump and hold it. After a minute remove the jigger and let the iodine run off into the bedding. Be careful not to spill the iodine down the foal's belly or inside its hind legs. If you do, you will blister the skin. It may cause an open sore, which will be a point of entry for bacteria.

Another method is to soak a cotton ball with iodine and hold it against the stump. You may want to wear surgical gloves because the iodine will stain your hands. Pour a little more iodine on the cotton as you're holding it, but don't pour so much that it overflows onto the foal's skin.

After you have disinfected the navel stump, move the foal around in front of his mother. She needs to see the foal at this point. Pick up his forelegs at the fetlock joints like you would grasp wheelbarrow handles and pull the foal toward you. You'll be backing up as you pull him around to the mare's head. It doesn't matter if the foal's belly or back faces her. Just place him where she can reach him to lick the eyes, ears, back and tail. She wants to take care of him and this attention will help dry him off and stimulate his systems. If the mare does not lick the foal thoroughly enough to dry him or if it's quite cold, help dry the foal by rubbing his body gently with a clean bath towel.

Whenever the mare is ready to get to her feet, be still and allow her to do so. She will not step on the foal. The only way she might step on her foal is if you rush at her or do something to alarm her, causing her to jump in fear. Just be quiet and let the mare relax. I've never seen a foal stepped on in this situation.

The mare needs to see her newborn foal. Her licking will dry the foal, stimulate it's systems and strengthen the bond between mother and foal. *(Photo courtesy of Martin Pierce)*

Problem Deliveries: Mares that foal right on schedule usually give birth uneventfully. Most problems occur in mares that go past their due dates. When a mare is overdue, place her under constant supervision and call the veterinarian at the first sign of trouble.

Trouble in foaling almost always comes in the form of bad presentations. If the foal is not in the correct position to be born - and there is only one right position - it can become wedged in the birth canal. Bad presentations include a foal with one or both forelegs folded backwards, the head turned back, the hips locked behind the mare's pelvis, a foal upside down or coming hindquarters first.

Bad presentations can be fatal to both mare and foal unless help arrives at the start of the trouble. Trapped trying to pass through the pelvis, the foal may die quickly if the umbilical cord is pinched. The mare will continue to push and strain until she damages herself, sometimes so severely that she must be put down. Because a bad presentation is so serious, all mares are checked by the foaling man soon after labor begins. At this early stage, he will know if he can correct the problem by turning the foal or if the situation requires veterinary help.

The veterinarian must be called at the first sign of trouble. The delivery process must be interrupted by walking the mare until the veterinarian arrives. Keeping the mare walking is of utmost importance. If the mare is up and walking around, she cannot push and make her situation worse. Do not allow her to lay down and strain. *She must be kept up and walking.*

A few foaling mares will have such difficult presentations that an attending veterinarian cannot correct the problem on the farm. The only hope for these mares and foals is a trip to a nearby veterinary hospital for a Caesarian section.

Another cause for concern is a delay in the second stage of labor. The mare may have a normal presentation but, after the water breaks, the delivery process stops. This is a dangerous situation and a veterinarian must be called immediately. A delay can kill the foal and injure the mare permanently.

What constitutes a delay? No one can say exactly how long. But keep in mind that delivery lasts only 30 to 45 minutes. After the water breaks, if you see that the birth is not progressing, if she does not lay down and push in the next five to 10 minutes, send an assistant to call the veterinarian. The veterinarian will come right out, either to find a healthy foal on the ground or to assist the mare while there's still time. Don't delay getting veterinary help - make the call.

The veterinarian can save most difficult births if he is on hand early enough. The majority of foaling deaths are not due to the hopelessness of the situation. They occur because the mare was left unattended - even for a half hour - and the foaling process had advanced to a point where nothing could be done to help the mare or foal. Preparation and vigilance will prevent most foaling mishaps.

Afterbirth: The only time a mare might unintentionally injure her foal is soon after delivery when she's in pain while shedding the afterbirth. Her uterus will contract painfully in an attempt to expel the afterbirth. She may appear colicky, going down several times. She may even roll and kick. If the mare is in pain, move the foal away from the middle of the stall. Stand between mother and foal, but don't take the foal out of the stall. That will needlessly stress the mare.

Expulsion of the afterbirth usually occurs within the first two hours after delivery. Sometimes it takes several hours, but the process becomes more risky with each passing hour. Because the tissues of the afterbirth decompose quickly, the mare must expel the entire afterbirth within eight hours of foaling. If the mare has not expelled the afterbirth after three hours, call the veterinarian. He will know how and when to remove it. He may decide to wait for another hour or so, but he'll understand what's happening and how to treat the mare. This is not a job for you or the foaling man. Let the veterinarian take care of this.

As she's shedding the afterbirth, tie it up above her hocks so she can't step on it. Use part of her tail wrap or clean gauze to tie it. Keep it from hitting her legs and keep her from stepping on it. *Never* apply traction to the afterbirth. Don't pull on it as you're tying it up. Doing so can permanently damage the mare's uterus.

When the afterbirth is shed, take it out of the stall and examine it carefully. It will look like a big pair of pants, with small, slim legs (one leg larger than the other) that are closed at the bottom. Like pants, it will be open at the top where the foal came out. Double-check that it's all there, including the horns, which are the "legs." If one leg is open at its end, the afterbirth is incomplete. Any afterbirth - even a small piece - remaining inside the mare can make her extremely sick, affect her fertility or even cause her to founder.

The color of a normal afterbirth is somewhere between pink and a light red. It should not be dark red or brown. Suspect trouble if you see a dark color. Get your scale out and weigh the afterbirth. It should weigh 12 to 16 pounds for a 100-pound foal. Healthy afterbirth is thin and pliable. If it's thick and quite heavy, say 22 pounds and the color is off, this indicates an infection. In such cases, the veterinarian should examine the mare and the foal. He may prescribe antibiotics for either mare and foal or for both. The mare that has produced an unhealthy afterbirth will not be ready to breed back on the foal heat.

Have the veterinarian examine the afterbirth, too. He may notice that a portion is missing or see something abnormal that you missed. Keep the afterbirth in good condition for the veterinarian if he can't get there right away. Putting it in a pail of cold water will preserve it and keep it from decomposing.

Nursing: Nursing is your new foal's first challenge. Achieving this goal will test his strength and your patience. Most foals will stand up an hour or so after birth, looking for the udder, but some are naturally slower than others. Don't be too anxious and don't try to force the foal to nurse. I give them about four hours to find it themselves. I might go in and hold the foal up and encourage him by putting his head in the right place. The hungrier he gets, the more eagerly he'll search for the nipple.

Collect any leaking colostrum. If the foal hasn't nursed after five hours, you may have a weak foal. At this point, the veterinarian is needed to tube-feed him. This requires use of the colostrum collected from the leaking mare and may further require milking the mare by hand. Have the colostrum ready before the foal gets too weak. (Of course, you have your supply of frozen colostrum, too.) All foals should receive colostrum within the first 15 hours.

Some people bottle-feed weak foals. This is acceptable if you can't get a veterinarian to tube-feed the foal. But I don't like to use the bottle because I don't think foals always swallow correctly drinking this way. They can inhale milk into the lungs and get pneumonia. The foal has an instinctive urge to suckle. He needs to learn to satisfy that urge from the mare's udder, not from a human with a baby bottle.

Occasionally a maiden mare will have a painfully tight udder. She might kick at the foal when he first tries to nurse. She must be restrained as gently as possible. Try holding one front foot up or lifting and squeezing a fold of skin on her shoulder. Don't twitch a mare that has just foaled. A twitch is too stressful. If you cannot persuade the mare to accept nursing her foal, the veterinarian can give her a mild drug. Occasionally this treatment is administered to nervous maiden mares and it works quite well. The veterinarian uses a mild sedative that will not harm the mare or foal. You won't have to do this too many times. When the pressure of the full udder is relieved, the mare will come around and accept the foal.

Sometimes a foal will have difficulty nursing because the mare's nipples are too small. The foal whose dam has small nipples will learn where the milk is but may need your help to stay on. Given the time and the strength to persevere, nature will take over. The act of nursing will elongate the nipples and the problem will correct itself.

Enemas: Every foal needs an enema after he's finished nursing for the first time. A foal that is lifting his tail and straining before nursing needs an enema right away.

I have a recipe and a method for giving enemas that works well. Take a quart can, or one of the special enema kits that comes with a can, and fill it 3/4 full of warm water. Add 1/4 cup of mineral oil and half a cake of Ivory soap. Prepare this ahead of time so the Ivory soap has time to dissolve in the water. The enema kit comes with a long, flexible tube, about three feet long to insert - gently - about 2 to 3 inches into the foal's rectum. Hold the can up to about the level of your shoulder - the liquid in the can goes down the tube and into the foal. It runs in and flushes out the fecal balls. I prefer this tube method to the enemas prepared for humans because it gets behind the fecal balls and flushes them out.

After you've administered the first enema, continue to watch the foal. If you see him straining or wringing his tail, give him another one, even if he passed fecal matter with the first enema. Don't wait until he's in pain, laying on his back and kicking. By that time the foal is in real danger from the constipation, so don't hesitate to give a second enema. If the constipation persists, call your veterinarian. He may want to examine the foal and take further measures.

Blood Tests and First Veterinarian Check: Sometime during the foal's first 24 hours, the veterinarian should examine the foal and draw blood for an IgG test. The IgG test checks for the passive transfer of antibodies which tells if the foal received the benefit of the colostrum. For an accurate reading, the blood must be taken 12 to 24 hours after the first nursing. After the first 12 hours, the foal's intestines begin to lose their "permeable" quality which makes it difficult for the foal to receive the benefits of the colostrum.

A high IgG level (greater than 400) indicates the foal is protected from serious infection. If the IgG test indicates that the foal did not receive the benefit of the colostrum, immediate steps must be taken to protect the foal. The foal's ability to benefit from colostrum begins to diminish by the 15th hour and is gone by 24 hours. If the foal is considerably less than 24 hours old, his intestines may still be permeable enough to benefit from colostrum from a donor mare. The veterinarian will tube-feed the colostrum to the foal. But if the foal is close to or more than 24 hours old, the veterinarian must administer blood plasma which contains the vital antibodies. Which method the veterinarian uses will depend on how close to 24 hours old the foal is and upon the veterinarian's best judgment. The majority of IgG tests come back showing a good passive transfer of antibodies, but if a mare has gone past her due date and her colostrum has been leaking, her foal may need one of these two therapies.

The veterinarian will examine the newborn foal, checking the eyes, looking for hernias, checking the umbilicus for bleeding and listening to the heart, lungs and stomach. He will check the foal's gums and other mucus membranes for color. A pink color indicates a healthy foal. A yellowish color indicates that the foal may have jaundice. Even though the mare was tested a month before foaling, the veterinarian will draw blood and test for jaundice if he sees this yellow color. A dark red color to the gums suggests that the foal may have suffered from a lack of oxygen or has an infection. Again, he can take measures to help this condition.

The veterinarian may give the foal a shot of *Combiotic*™ or a similar antibiotic. This is an optional procedure for the normal foal. Depending on the farm manager and the veterinarian involved, normal, healthy foals may receive no antibiotics. I don't believe in giving antibiotics to every foal "just in case." Indiscriminate use of antibiotics may cause more problems than it prevents. If you have a strong foal and the birth was perfect, you probably don't need to give him antibiotics.

A weak foal or one whose afterbirth didn't look right, needs a complete antibiotic program for as long as 10 days. Consult your veterinarian for a program of antibiotics and special monitoring. Don't try to cut corners and treat a weak newborn yourself.

Monitoring the Foal: Take the foal's temperature each morning and evening so you have a baseline. The average temperature of horses will vary from 99 to 101 degrees. Establishing what is normal for a particular foal will help you know if he's sick. A one-degree rise in temperature should be reported to the foaling man or farm manager, and a rise of two degrees to the veterinarian. A temperature of 102 or 103 is cause for concern, and the foal needs veterinary attention. If you do not catch this right away, the temperature can spike rapidly to 104 degrees. Now the foal is definitely ill and not nursing. Foals can become ill very quickly and are much better off if you catch a problem early.

A good indicator of the health of the foal is the mare's udder. Experienced foaling men know that a full udder is often the first sign of trouble with the foal. Healthy foals nurse frequently, as often as every 30 minutes for newborns. They keep the udder drained, giving it a fairly flat appearance. Each time you check the mare and foal, take a look at her udder to confirm that the foal is nursing.

Evaluate the legs of the foal soon after birth for straightness and strength. Some foals are born with contracted tendons and others may be knock-kneed. Both conditions require special veterinary help. However, some foals look like wrecks shortly after birth, then improve dramatically in a few days. The veterinarian knows if and when a foal needs special help with its legs. For a more complete discussion of leg problems in foals, see *Monitoring the Legs* later in this chapter.

Leading the Newborn: When the foal has nursed and napped a few times, move the mare and foal from the foaling stall into the mare's regular stall. It's best to get them into a natural environment as quickly as possible. The foal doesn't need the artificial warmth of the foaling stall. He'll benefit from the ventilation of his dam's regular stall and from having the barn doors open. You'll see that even the youngest foals are comfortable with this.

Leading the newborn foal and his dam into their own stall for the first time takes two people. One person leads the mare, another cradles the foal by putting an arm around the chest and around the rump, gently urging him forward or holding him back with the appropriate arm. The person leading the mare opens the stall door.

Foals are energetic and easily distracted. When leading mares and foals, keep the foal close to his mother. Nature tells the mare to not allow the newborn foal out of her sight. If you respect this instinct, you avoid needless stress to both. The mare relaxes her vigilance in a few weeks when the foal is stronger. Your foal may not follow right behind his dam. He may shoot off in any of 360 degrees, so be prepared. If the foal lags behind, slow the mare down so they aren't separated by more than a few feet. Occasionally, an exuberant foal will become airborne and loosen his handler's hold. The mare handler can provide momentary reinforcement in such an event. The way to handle the mare and newborn foal is gently and easily, so use competent assistants and take your time.

Hemorrhage in the Mare: The risk of hemorrhage in the mare exists for the first day or two following birth. Hemorrhage in the foaling mare is not a routine occurrence but it does happen, especially in older mares. Some mares have weak blood vessels that break and bleed easily under the pressures of foaling. In the worst case, the uterine artery or another large blood vessel ruptures and the blood spills into the abdomen, killing the mare quickly. A less extensive hemorrhage - one that bleeds into the broad uterine ligament or into uterine muscle - can be treated if caught in time. If the veterinarian administers medication to treat a mild hemorrhage in the first half hour, the mare may be saved. But waiting an hour or two for veterinary attention or turning out the hemorrhaging mare can cost the mare's life.

Usually a hemorrhaging mare has whitish or off-color gums, while a healthy mare has pink gums. Gum color is often the first indication of trouble. One of your first steps after the birth is to check the mare's gums for color. If she's an older mare, say 15 or 20, watch her carefully and check her gums often during the first few hours. If she seems well, you can cut back the frequency of the checks, but continue to monitor the mare for the first day or two. Each time you pass the stall and look in on the foal, go in and roll back the mare's lip to check the color of her gums.

Colicky, dull or shocky behavior may also signal hemorrhage. If you see these symptoms or if her gums have lost color, call the veterinarian immediately. Then take steps to minimize stress to the mare. Darken the stall, close all windows and doors and stop all traffic past her stall. Do not move her foal out of the stall. The hemorrhaging mare needs absolute quiet - do nothing that would cause her to even lift her head. Early treatment by the veterinarian and appropriate management is the only chance to save a hemorrhaging mare.

Sometimes there is no outward sign that a mare is hemorrhaging until she is in shock and near death. At this point, it is too late for any treatment. Hemorrhage in mares, like heart attacks in humans, will be with us for a long time. You can't predict that it will happen and there is no way to prevent it from starting. But understanding the risk and good management will save some mares. Minimizing stress to the post-foaling mare and calling the veterinarian immediately can keep a small hemorrhage from becoming a fatal one.

Patent Urachus: A problem that afflicts a few newborn foals is patent urachus. The urachus is the small, temporary structure for the excretion of urine while the foal is in the uterus. After birth, when the umbilical cord is severed, the urachus should close up. Urine then passes through the urethra, as in adult horses. In a case of patent urachus, this tube fails to close and urine passes through the umbilical stump. The constant dribbling of urine from the umbilical stump prevents it from healing and allows bacteria to enter the bladder, causing cystitis and other serious problems. This condition requires veterinary treatment.

Check the umbilical stump to see that it's drying up properly, which usually takes three or four days. Watch for any urine dribbling from the navel stump. If you suspect the foal may have patent urachus, call the veterinarian immediately.

Foal Scours: Almost all foals develop diarrhea, or foal scours, sometime between the seventh and the 15th day. The diarrhea is a yellowish color and usually coincides with the mare's foal heat.

It's not certain what causes foal scours. It might be dietary, from the foal eating his mother's food or manure. Some people think there's something in the mare's milk during the heat that causes it. Others believe that the foal picks up bacteria from the heat discharge that runs down from the vagina to the udder. Some veterinarians recommend washing the mare from stem to stern every day during foal heat to reduce this contamination. Parasites are occasionally blamed for foal scours. I don't know if any of these theories are true.

The only thing you need to do is to keep the diarrhea from scalding the foal's bottom. Keep him clean, keep the diarrhea out of his tail and keep his rump greased with mineral oil so he isn't burned. If you see the foal cramping or acting colicky, inform the veterinarian. He can give the foal some milk of magnesia or other medication that will help him through it.

Scours during foal heat is the only time the foal should have any diarrhea. Any other time you see diarrhea, or any sign of digestive trouble, call the veterinarian right away. Foals can go downhill awfully fast, so don't waste even five minutes getting help.

Turn Out: If the mare foaled during the night and she and the foal appear healthy in the morning, turn them out in a paddock by themselves. A good, strong foal that has nursed in his first three hours may go out for an hour or so with his mother. The mare needs to go out and exercise lightly. Exercise helps her "throw off" the fluids, which is the cleansing process of the reproductive organs. She will have an odorless vaginal discharge about the color and consistency of chocolate syrup. This is a normal process. The sooner she can exercise, the better it is for her long-term health as a broodmare.

The rule of thumb for weather above 40 degrees is that they may stay out for most of the day. Colder than 40 degrees, they should be out less than an hour. The use of a round pen or exercise pavilion can extend the turn out time in foul weather. In any case, the newborn foal should ultimately decide the duration of the turnout. Mare and foal must come in before the foal becomes tired.

The first time out, release the mare carefully, especially if this is her first foal. Have someone hold the foal out of the way where the mare can see it before releasing her. If she kicks out, you don't want the foal in the way. After the first turn out, she'll remember she has a foal and will act more responsibly.

The mare probably will run up and down the paddock once or twice, then settle down and graze. This is what you hope she'll do. But if the mare doesn't stop running, she and her foal must come back inside. The newborn foal will run too much trying to keep up with his dam and it will place too much stress on him. This stress can weaken the foal and make him more susceptible to illness. I think the foal can even damage his tendons, bones or cartilage when he runs to the point of exhaustion. You may not find out how much damage was done until much later. By then it's too late. It's a mistake to let the mare run all over the paddock for the first few days with her foal trying to keep up and getting tired.

Certain things may cause the mare to become unsettled and run too much. Putting her out with or next to a strange mare or out with the herd too soon may excite her. Keep her where she can't see or hear the teaser. Keep dogs away from her. She is afraid of the teaser and of dogs, so protect her. Keep her alone with her foal for a few days. It's a time to keep the mare quiet.

My philosophy for turning out mares and foals is to keep them within the same herd. A group of five or six pregnant mares that got along with one another should be maintained together when their foals come. Don't mix them with new mares or disperse them to another group of horses. Apart from the psychological stress of different companions, I believe that mares and foals remain healthier if no new additions are made to their group. The newborn has a lot to overcome when he enters the world and introducing a new mare to an established group adds contamination in the form of new bacteria and viruses.

After the mare and foal have been out seven days and are settled comfortably in their own paddock, you may add one of her former pasturemates and her foal. On the 10th day, add another mare and foal. If all goes smoothly, add another pair each day until the original herd of five or six mares is reunited.

Mares and foals should come inside the barn every night during the early spring. When the hours of daylight have lengthened to equal the hours of darkness, around April 15, mares and foals may stay out in the pasture at night, weather permitting. Mares and foals should still come into the barn once a day for a meal and to be checked carefully. Continue to take the foal's temperature daily and monitor the mare's udder. Train yourself to look for problems so they can be dealt with immediately. Good management starts with keen observation.

During the hot, humid weather of summer, mares and foals should be brought into the barn during the day. The barn offers relief from the heat and from the insects in the pasture that cause them to stomp and fret. Turn them out at night when they can be comfortable outside again.

Haltering the Foal: When to first put a halter on a foal is a subject of some debate. Some horsemen halter the newborn for the first trip outside while others prefer to wait a few days until the foal is stronger. I've done it both ways and the best method depends on the individual foal. A weak or timid foal may benefit from a few days delay, but a vigorous, headstrong foal can wear a halter his first day. Generally, the third day is a safe time to introduce the halter to the average foal.

It is important that the halter fit correctly. A proper foal halter is lightweight, made of soft leather and is adjustable. It must fit closely enough around the throat and chin so the foal cannot put his hind foot inside it. A design like a calf halter which forms a figure-eight works well. Adjust the halter every fourth day for the first two weeks and every week for the following two or three weeks. The foal's head grows rapidly for the first month or so and the halter must not become too snug.

Another important halter feature is the size of the ring onto which the lead shank is snapped. This ring must be large enough that to allow you to open the snap on the lead shank, hook it over the ring and let the snap close without touching the foal or his whiskers. If you accidently pull the whiskers every time you catch the foal, he will soon learn that being caught is painful. Like any intelligent, sensitive animal, he will avoid what hurts him and you'll have a dickens of a time catching him. He should not associate people with pain. Make every experience with humans pleasant and soothing for the foal.

This halter fits this foal. The lead shank can be attached to the halter ring without pulling the foal's whiskers.
(Photo courtesy of Martin Pierce)

Leading lessons: The first time the foal wears a halter to go outside with his dam have one person lead the mare and a second person lead the foal. The man leading the foal holds the lead shank attached to the halter in his left hand and a large, soft rope around the foal's rump in his right hand. This soft rope gives the handler control if the foal balks or backs up. The rope allows the handler to gently urge the foal forward, the rope pressure corresponding with gentle tugs on the halter. These two simultaneous actions are the start of training to lead. The foal associates the gentle tugs with pressure from behind and moves ahead, giving to the halter. Continue using the rump rope until the foal understands the pressure from the halter.

When teaching the foal to lead, avoid letting him pull back against the halter. If a foal panics and lunges backward, give slack to the shank and step back with him until you regain control. A panicky foal pulling back against the halter can slip, fall down or flip over backwards. The result can be a serious, career-ending injury.

By the fourth or fifth day, the mare and foal can be led by one person holding both shanks. The handler stands with the foal at his immediate right, holding the foal's shank in his right hand. To the right of the foal is the mare, her shank held in the handler's left hand. The foal is "sandwiched" between his dam on the right and the handler on his left. With his options for movement limited, the foal will walk to the paddock alongside the handler and his dam.

This timetable works if you have a good, safe environment and experienced personnel. If you lack either one, or if you are not confident that they can be led safely by one person, use extra people. Foals are energetic and easily distracted. A loose foal will find some way to hurt himself given the smallest opportunity.

Foal Care When Rebreeding the Mare: Modern breeding practices dictate that the mare comes to the stallion. Common sense says that a mare being shipped a long distance will depart with her foal. But a mare being bred to a stallion 10 miles away will leave her foal at home. The question is what to do with the foal while his dam is being covered.

Separate the mare and foal so they cannot hear one another. After the mare is on the van and a few miles down the road, she will settle down. Put the foal in a clean, empty stall that has no buckets, feed tubs or other hazards. Have a groom or other experienced handler keep an eye on him. The foal will cry, run around and stand on his hind legs but, with supervision, this is the safest method.

In those instances when the foal accompanies the mare, he should not go into the breeding shed with her. I have heard of a foal being held some yards in front of the mare during the cover, but this is not good management. The sight and sound of the foal will upset and distract the mare. She may reject and attempt to kick the stallion, regardless of how ready she is for breeding. This is not only a waste of a good cover, but a dangerous situation as well. You risk not getting the mare bred, the mare kicking the stallion, the foal getting loose and everyone - handlers included - being injured.

Feeding the Foal: When the foal is six weeks old, begin feeding it some grain. Use a feed specially made for nursing foals, and start with a small amount, about a teacup full. Use a small bucket, commonly called a "foal cup." Hang the cup inside the stall while the mare eats her grain. You don't want the mare raiding the foal's feed, so it may help to tie her during mealtime. Tie her with a light chain and a piece of string - not baling twine - attaching the chain to a screw-eye, mounted on the wall about 4 1/2 feet high. If the mare pulls back, the string will break and the chain will dangle harmlessly. Never use baling or binder twine to tie the mare - the foal could easily get caught in the sturdy twine and strangle. When the mare has finished her grain, remove the foal cup, whether the foal has finished eating or not. Don't leave the foal's food in the stall for the mare to eat or let it sit out where it may spoil. Always feed fresh grain for each meal.

I do not creep-feed my foals. Creep-feeding allows foals to walk under a special fence that their dams cannot pass under and eat grain free-choice. While many farms successfully creep-feed their foals, I prefer to control the amount of feed given to each foal.

In my experience, foals that incur developmental disorders are usually the biggest, growthiest ones on the farm. These foals grow rapidly on a small or moderate amount of feed. Although these big foals need less feed than the other foals, creep-feeding allows them to consume more. Giving them all they can eat might "push them over the line" and cause growth disorders. Many times, these "big eaters" are the most valuable foals on the farm, so we don't take the risk of creep-feeding them.

The risks of overfeeding young horses are very real. The damage is slow and insidious - often, the problem is not apparent until the horse breaks down in training. The problems caused by overfeeding and unbalanced rations and the way to avoid these problems, are explained in the chapter *Feeding Horses*.

Handling the Foal's Feet: After the foal is accustomed to the halter for about two weeks, start handling his legs and feet. Run your hand down the inside of his legs daily and try to gently pick up a foot. Let the foal put it down as soon as he yields it to you. Gradually extend the time you hold up the foot. It may help to have another person steady the foal's balance as you do this. The foal's balance will improve with each week of life. As he approaches 30 days old, he is able to stand on three legs for five or 10 seconds, provided he's had the proper training.

Foals need to be seen by the farrier every 30 days. Many should not be trimmed this often, as overzealous trimming is as harmful as outright neglect. But have the foal looked at regularly. The farrier may say "let him go another month," but do not skip the exam.

Learning to stand for the farrier is an important part of the foal's education. It is much easier to accomplish this and produce a mannerly horse if you start when they're small and impressionable. Make this experience easier for him by teaching the foal to stand still and by rubbing and brushing him in the stall. Gentle brushing, rubbing or scratching in the stall teaches the foal to trust people and submit to their directions. Our foals are photographed every month, so they learn about standing still early in life.

Handling and gentling the foal will facilitate the series of vaccinations that must begin at 30 days (See *General Farm Routine* chapter). If your only contact with the foal is grabbing him and holding him down for a shot, he will become wary and distrustful of humans. Your veterinarian may have a change in attitude as he attempts to vaccinate a flying target. Teaching the foal manners produces a safer horse to work around, benefiting your staff as much as the foal.

Monitoring the Legs: Many foals are born with temporary leg problems or weaknesses. Some newborn foals are "down on their pasterns," meaning that the fetlock sags toward the ground. This usually disappears in a few days, but those foals that are walking on their fetlocks need protective bandaging so they don't scrape the skin off the fetlock. Other weaknesses include knock-knees, sprung knees, capped elbows and hocks and slightly curby or rounded hocks. By the time the foal is several days old, the temporary leg problems and weaknesses of birth should have disappeared or be rapidly improving. These problems usually show rapid improvement in a few weeks.

More severe leg problems are calf-knees (back at the knee), severe knock knees and knees that are bow-legged, the opposite of knock knees. Foals that toe in or out severely, that have contracted tendons or that knuckle over in the fetlock and foals with bowed hind legs may have serious problems, also.

The farm manager should check the legs of every nursing foal daily until they become weanlings. It requires an experienced eye to recognize if the foal is making satisfactory progress and growth. Many need only a little careful, corrective rasping of their hooves to develop strong, straight legs. Foals with severe leg problems need to be examined regularly by a veterinarian who specializes in this area of practice. There are several things that can be done to correct severely crooked legs, but they must be done in a timely fashion. There are periods of rapid growth when corrective surgery is most effective. Foals with crooked legs can grow into straight yearlings with little or no signs of the defect or its repair, but only with expert, timely intervention and follow-up.

It is a good practice to photograph the foal at regular intervals. A picture taken every month helps to show if the foal's legs are straightening out at a satisfactory rate. It is easy to imagine that the foal is making progress when he is not. A series of photographs is a good tool for determining if he is developing properly or if he needs veterinary intervention.

Periosteal Stripping: One of the best tools for correcting crooked legs is periosteal stripping. Simply described, periosteal stripping means to surgically cut the outer layer of bone (periosteum) on one side of the leg. The cuts are made just above the growth plate, which encourages that side of the leg to grow faster. A knock-kneed foal would have this done right above his knees, on the outside.   As growth is accelerated on the outside of the legs, they straighten up. Some foals may need this surgery twice. But it is a non-invasive procedure and relatively inexpensive. It is amazing what a good veterinarian who specializes this field can accomplish. Those crooked legs can be made to straighten right up without even a tell-tale scar. And the procedure will not over-correct the leg.

Mudding the Foals' Legs: Foals are particularly vulnerable to the effects of flies biting their legs. Foals will stomp their feet to shake off the flies. Many will stomp until their legs are crooked or are damaged permanently. We have a special little gimmick to overcome this problem. We keep foals' legs coated with a mud poultice. It covers the legs from above the knee to below the ankle and they wear this mixture every day, all day. The mud prevents the flies from biting the foals' legs which eliminates the stomping. We start mudding the foals in early May and continue into the fall. If the bot flies are bad, we'll continue it until the first freeze in October.

The recipe for our mud poultice is simple. Take a 50 lb. bag of mud, like *Kentucky Track Mud*™, and pour half the bag into a five gallon pail. Add a teacup full of alum, a quart of vinegar and enough water to make a mud-like consistency. Mix it up well. This yields a bucket 2/3 full of mud, enough to do about 40 foals. Apply this mixture to the legs. Put it on thick because some of it is bound to wear off. Wash it off and put on a fresh coat about twice a week. In between muddings, patch the thin spots.

It takes a little time to get this on the foals' legs at first. They want to pull their legs away and dance around. Arm yourself with patience, because these are valuable lessons for the impressionable young foal. Gradually, they become accustomed to having their legs handled. They even begin to like it. This pays dividends when the farrier comes to trim them.   Another benefit is that minor leg problems, such as small splints, are detected sooner with this mudding procedure. The veterinarian appreciates finding problems while they are small and treatable and he appreciates the training that foals get by being mudded.

We also use this mud on some of the yearlings. Some of these young horses have growth spurts.   Their joints are open and vulnerable to epiphysitis.   This mud poultice prevents them from damaging the joints by stamping. If the knees or ankles are a little swollen or knobby, it seems to cool and tighten them.

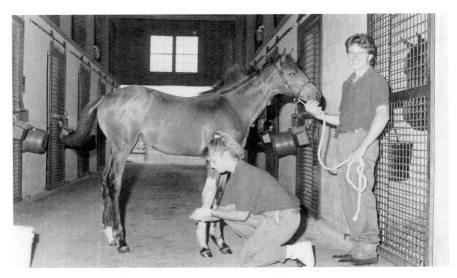

Mudding the foals' legs offers many benefits.

(Photo courtesy of Joy Gilbert)

Weaning: There is no shortage of myths, superstitions and old wives' tales about weaning. It's no wonder, since weaning is the single, most traumatic event in a horse's life. The shock and anxiety to both the freshly weaned foal and mare are profound and heartrending. The high incidence of injury, disease and foal loss during weaning have led breeders to speculate over the years as to what causes these unfortunate occurrences. Ignorance of the real cause leads people to focus on such irrelevant factors as the position of the moon.

It is the stress of weaning that causes problems for both foals and mares. Stress is the real reason foals become sick and injure themselves. Mares abort from the stress of weaning. If we eliminate most of the stress of weaning, we eliminate most of the risk.

We stagger our weanings throughout the fall so we are not weaning all the foals at the same time. We begin weaning the first batch of foals in late August or early September. By this time the January foals will be eight or nine months old and the extremely hot weather of summer is usually past. If not, wait a few weeks for more moderate temperatures. Hot weather is too stressful for weaning. Five months is the minimum age to consider weaning a foal. October is the time to wean June foals, so they have the benefit of five months with their dams.

We wean our foals in the evening. A good, tranquil time is towards the end of an evening meal, fed in the pasture. After the mare has eaten but while her foal is still eating, remove the mare from the group. Lead her away as quietly as possible and put her on a van. Ship her to another part of the farm where she is out of earshot of the foal. It is important that she not hear her foal and vice versa. If they can hear and respond to one another's whinnies, the screaming will last for hours or even days. The mare must be kept where she cannot hear her foal. Then she will settle down quickly.

When her foal has finished his meal, he finds himself out with the other mares and foals. Although his dam is gone, the foal is in the same field with the same mares and foals he has known all his life. The familiarity of his surroundings reassures him and he won't panic. In the past, he has probably attempted to nurse from some of the other mares. He may try this again, with or without success, but it is business as usual. He will not be frantic. The other foals satisfy his need for companionship, he has just eaten and there are big mare bodies to run behind if he feels threatened. Seeing his companions calm and content and seeing that his environment is unchanged, the foal adjusts quickly.

You may notice that the foal is a little nervous the first day, but by the second day he will settle down and he will be hungry. He should come into the barn every day with the others for a meal and be fed in his own stall, which is the same stall he shared with his dam. The less change in the routine, the less stress experienced by the foal.

Foals should be fed an 18% protein grain mixture, made specifically for weanlings (See Chapter 14, *Feeding Horses*). Offer him about a pound to a pound and a half. If he needs more, he will tell you. If he can't eat this much, cut back the amount until he cleans up what you give him. In a week or so, he may need the amount of feed increased.

The mare needs special attention during this period of adjustment. She needs to be turned out, not put into a stall. Her feed should be reduced sharply to grass hay, lean pasture and no grain at all. She may refuse to eat for several hours, preferring to run the fence. It is not a problem if she refuses to eat for several hours, but don't forget about her. She will be nervous and agitated, so treat her gently. Offer her some hay, speak to her or stand with her if it calms her down. This is a difficult time for her, so treat her with sympathy and understanding.

Some of the mare's misery during weaning is due to a tight, swollen udder. Begin monitoring the udder that first evening of separation. It is a good practice to rub her udder with some mineral oil or camphor gum as soon as she will permit it. The next day her udder will be tight. Apply more mineral oil, but don't milk her. Milking only stimulates the production of more milk, prolonging the drying-up period. However uncomfortable she looks, milking her will only make it worse. Turnout and no grain are what is needed to shrink the udder. Grain stimulates the mare's system to begin milk production again. Eliminate her grain for at least 10 days and possibly as long as three weeks. It will take about five days for the udder to show signs of shrinking to a pre-foaling condition, so be patient. After a week or 10 days of this restricted diet, the mare will have settled down and her udder will be shrinking up nicely. Those mares whose foals are eight months old have an easier time drying up than those with five-month-old foals. They have less distension and tenderness.

Check the mare's udder several times a day during the drying up period. Report any extreme heat or tenderness to the veterinarian. Heat or pain could be a sign of mastitis, which is serious and must be treated immediately. Mastitis is not uncommon in horses.

After the first foal is successfully weaned, you may wean another by removing a second mare. The procedure is the same. Now you have three mares and five foals in one pasture. The two solitary foals may pair up and spend their days grazing close to one another. This may change with the subsequent weanings, but the motherless foals will sort out the alliances and pecking order among themselves.

As you remove the mares from the group, you may see that certain foals have "buddied up." While the rule is to feed the foal in the same stall he shared with his dam, you may find that putting two buddies next to or across from one another is a good arrangement. Many farms put two foals in a stall together to ease the anxiety of separation from their dams. It does soothe the foals to be together in one stall but, months later, you're faced with another weaning. Save this solution for the rare foal that is truly frantic and put the rest of the foals in their own stalls. The rules are made to reduce stress on the young horses. If bending a rule or changing a practice results in less stress, by all means do it.

A critical time is reached when only one mare and foal remain to be weaned. This foal is usually the youngest one in the group, perhaps a June foal. Delay weaning this foal as long as possible. The foals that have already been weaned are accustomed to the presence of the last mare. Depending on how tolerant she is, they may even nurse from her. They look to her for reassurance when they are frightened. During a storm, you might see them all clustered around her. Without the presence of the "baby-sitter mare," the foals may become so frightened during a bad storm that they may run through a fence. This last mare is important to the safety and stability of the group of weanlings. The older they are when you finally remove her, the better.

Proper Weanling Care: Between weaning and the start of yearling preparation lies a period of freedom for young horses. Their only task to grow and develop into strong, healthy yearlings and, for the most part, nature and good pastures are your best tools to help them do this. Your job is to keep them on the right track by feeding them well, keeping their feet correct and allowing them to grow up.

Diet is critical for the weanling because growth is rapid and nutritional needs are precise, but ever-changing. Like foals, all weanlings should be weighed, measured and photographed monthly. Work with your nutritional consultant to make sure the young horse is developing correctly. A slight adjustment in the feed mixture may be needed to encourage growth or to slow too rapid development. Give the weanlings a fresh pasture. Don't put them in a field that the yearlings have trampled. The nourishment and contentment they get from good pasture are two big factors in their proper development.

Separate weanlings by sex and turn them out in small groups of five or six. Pay attention to size and temperament. A small or timid weanling should not be turned out with larger colts that bully him. Weanlings should spend most of their first winter in the fields, where the fresh air and the room to gallop with their companions builds their bones and muscles. It is not necessary to blanket weanlings or keep them inside at night. In most weather, they are protected by their thick coats and are more comfortable staying outside. The only exceptions are hours of cold rain, freezing rain, wet snow or strong winds with sub-zero wind chill factors. In this weather, all horses need to be inside at night to dry off, eat and sleep. Lead the weanlings inside in pairs or groups. Never leave a single weanling in the field by itself.

Each morning, bring the weanlings inside the barn for feeding and a few hours of rest. Train the grooms to examine the young horses carefully each day. It is important to look beneath the long winter coat to see the true condition of the animal. Check coats for scabs or loose patches of hair which may indicate rainrot, a skin infection common in damp weather. Rainrot can be treated with a mixture of half mineral oil and half rubbing alcohol. This mixture is applied to the affected areas, the backbone and to the pastern area. The weanlings' feet should be picked out daily and the legs and feet examined carefully. Treat any cuts with nitrofurazone. Tail-chewing is usually prevented by supplying mineral blocks. Isolate the odd colt who persists in chewing the others' tails. A thermometer should always be handy in case any weanling seems off. Every few days, bring them all inside for inspection by the farm manager.

Weanlings should be groomed regularly and bathed in warm weather. It requires patience to teach them to submit to brushing and bathing, but time spent handling the weanlings will pay off when they are yearlings being prepped for the sales. If a weanling's legs were mudded as a foal, he has a head-start in this area. Weanlings must learn to stand squarely for inspections and photographs. They must be trained to walk off in a straight line and to halt straight. It takes time to teach the young horse how to present himself well, but this early training will pay dividends during preparation for the sales.

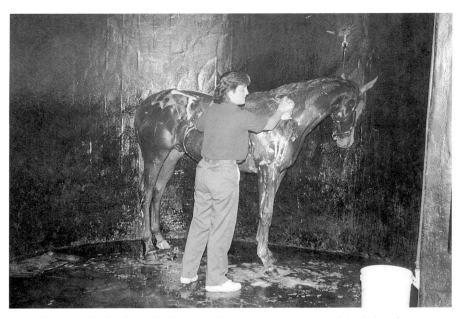

Regular baths benefit the weanling's appearance and training for sales preparation.
(Photo Courtesy of Joy Gilbert)

Chapter 11

Yearling Management

The yearling year is a critical stage for young racehorses and is a time of reckoning for their breeders. As many as 1/4 of the entire crop will pass through the auction rings of the summer and fall sales. Breeding decisions made more than two years previous will be affirmed or discredited. Breeders' fortunes and reputations will rise and fall with the auctioneer's hammer.

Early in the spring, yearlings nominated for sales are judged by the sales companies' pedigree experts. Yearlings with important pedigrees are evaluated on site by conformation experts. The results of the experts' findings on pedigree and conformation are given to the sales company's selection committee. Weighing pedigree against conformation, the committee decides which yearlings will be included in the select sales. While admission to these sales is a high honor, it is no dishonor to be excluded. Even the most successful breeders will have only a small percentage of their yearling crop qualify for the select sales.

Because yearling sales have such an impact on the industry, the preparation of sales yearlings is a specialized business. All yearlings must arrive at the sales at their individual peak of condition. Each youngster must be carefully fed, exercised and trained. Overfeeding or overconditioning will damage the young horse. Less than optimum nutrition or a lack of muscle-building activities will be penalized by lower bids. To bring each yearling to its physical peak within its genetic framework for size, strength and maturation is to strike a fine balance indeed.

Preparing the Yearling Mentally for the Sales and for Racing: The yearling year is a crucial time for more than economic reasons. It is the time to learn new lessons, some of which will be strange and frightening. Young Thoroughbreds and Standardbreds must learn the manners that make training possible and the attitude that can make them successful.

At this stage, mental preparation is as important - maybe more important - than physical training. No one can overpower a horse. Successful training for racing must enlist the horse's cooperation. A foundation must be laid to build a cooperative attitude. The horse must be made gentle and mannerly so he does not injure people or himself. This includes training to lead, stand, "set-up," be photographed and submit to all kinds of grooming and veterinary care. The horse must learn that while man is the dominant member of any herd, he is a fair and wise leader. This lesson is most important because it enables the young horse to relax and submit to being bridled, saddled, ridden and worked.

The importance of these early lessons cannot be overstated. The horse is not highly intelligent but he is sensitive, impressionable and has a superb memory. Everything that happens to him is recorded and retained and it is impossible to "erase" an unsuccessful training attempt. It must be done right the first time.

Round Pen Work: Our most important training and conditioning tool at *Taylor Made* is our round pen. We use the round pen to condition the horse's mind as well as his body. Round pen work lays the foundation for cooperation better than any other method I have seen in my 50 years in the racehorse business. It is safe, natural and effective.

We were introduced to round pen work by Monte Roberts, a famous horseman who has demonstrated the round pen technique to horsemen everywhere, including to the Queen of England. We were skeptical at first, since round pen training is so different from the traditional method of conditioning and breaking racehorses. But we were convinced by Mr. Robert's demonstrations. All the horses learned quickly, suffered no pain, injury or stress and retained the lessons to become more trainable racehorses.

Building the Round Pen: The round pen method requires that a round enclosure be built. The pen is 50 feet in diameter with walls at least eight feet high. The lumber for the walls must be two by six inches, strong enough to withstand a kick without cracking or splintering. The walls are solid from the ground up and there are no sharp edges or protrusions to injure the horse. Walls are tongue-in-groove construction, with no spaces or gaps that can catch the horse's foot. Make the door solid, without a handle inside and flush with the wall. The footing is sand or shavings that provides traction for the horse and protects his feet from concussion. The important features are the round shape that does not allow the horse to stop in the corner and the smooth, solid walls that protect him from injuring himself.

The interior of the roundpen shows that there is nothing to injure a horse. *(Photo courtesy of Suzie Oldham)*

The Basis of Round Pen Work: Round pen work is effective because it works with two strong, natural instincts of the horse: 1) the instinct to flee from what frightens him; and, 2) the instinct to be part of a herd.

A pastured horse that is frightened will run away from whatever he feels to be a threat. After he has run to what he feels is a safe distance, he will stop, turn and look at what startled him. The round pen method accommodates this instinct. It allows the horse to flee when he feels frightened and to stop when he feels safe enough to confront his fear.

Horses are herd animals and feel most secure when they are in the company of others. All herds have a hierarchy, a pecking order. There is one leader on whom the others depend for giving alarm, choosing when and where to eat and to drink. This fact is incorporated into the round pen method. By driving the horse away, the trainer establishes dominance over the horse - he becomes the herd leader. When the leader invites the horse to approach, he is saying, "Join my herd - there is no danger when you are with me. You can relax."

Round pen work is structured to use the two above basic instincts by applying the principle of advance and retreat. *Advance* simply means that the horse moves toward the trainer. *Retreat* means the horse moves away from the trainer. Each step of the round pen work begins with this simple proposition: come to me or go away. The horse's response indicates one of two things: (1) The horse holds his ground, then advances toward the trainer, meaning he accepts the lesson and, at this point, he participates in the training, or; (2) The horse ignores the trainer or moves away from the trainer, meaning that he does not accept the lesson and needs to circle the round pen without restraint for a longer period of time.

Throughout the process, the horse is given opportunities to decide whether to advance or to retreat. The round pen method is structured to provoke a response from the horse *at each stage*. By his actions, the horse says, "Yes, I will tolerate this in order to be with you," or, "I don't understand or accept your restraints - they frighten me or annoy me and I choose to move away from you." The freedom to decide, to choose to move away from what frightens him, enables the horse to overcome his fear and consciously participate in the training process. Since the horse indicates when he is ready to move on to the next step, he is never rushed or pushed ahead of his learning capacity.

Round pen training begins with the hooking up (which I shall explain shortly) and the first session lasts as long as necessary to achieve this step. Each successive day is devoted to learning a new lesson. Training proceeds on a daily basis until the horse has mastered the lessons that allow him to be bridled, saddled and ground-driven. All yearlings destined for the sales are taken through this stage of training.

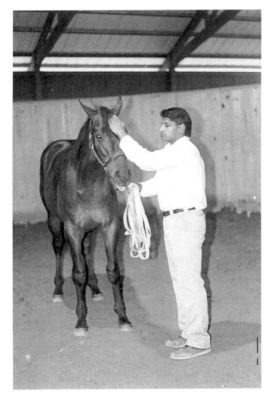

Step One: The horse is led into the round pen for the first time. He is released and allowed to look around and smell the enclosure until he appears comfortable. The trainer enters the round pen and approaches the horse to initiate a forehead rub, which reassures the horse. The trainer then turns and walks away. If the horse follows the trainer, he receives another forehead rub. These actions by the trainer tell the horse, "It is safe and pleasurable to be with me." This simple gesture of reassurance forms the foundation of trust for all the training that follows.

Step One: The trainer initiates a forehead rub.
(Photo courtesy of Suzie Oldham)

Step Two: If the horse ignores the trainer or refuses his approach, he is driven away by the trainer walking behind him and swinging or slapping a lunge line as he walks. The trainer's actions say, "If you don't want to be with me, then go away. These are your choices." The horse understands this simple proposition. He is free to gallop around the round pen until his excess energy is gone or until his curiosity overcomes his fear. When he is ready, he will relax and focus his attention on the trainer.

Step Two: The horse may decide to ignore the trainer, who will drive him away. Or, if the horse is frightened, he is allowed to run around the pen. Either response is a retreat - both lead to advancing toward the trainer. *(Photo courtesy of Suzie Oldham)*

Step Three: As the horse moves around the pen, the trainer watches the eyes and ears of the horse for signs of interest and submission. He is looking for the horse to watch him, face him, lower his head or snort. Periodically, the trainer will step in front of the horse, causing him to change direction. At some point, usually when changing direction, the horse will pause and look at the trainer. This tells the trainer that he may approach the horse in a non-threatening manner and rub the horse's forehead. The trainer drops the lunge line and approaches slowly, hand outstretched and avoiding eye contact. If the horse backs away, he is driven around again until the next indication of interest or submission.

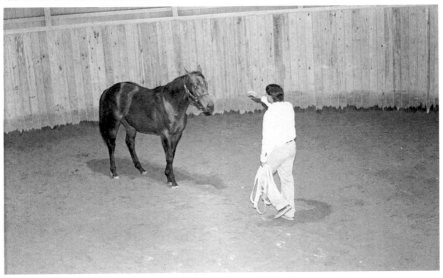

Step Three: The trainer has stepped in front of the horse to initiate a turn. The horse pauses and looks at the trainer, who approaches slowly with outstretched hand to offer a forehead rub.

(Photo courtesy of Suzie Oldham)

Step Four: The horse that refuses the trainer's outstretched hand and the forehead rub is driven away after each refusal. After circling the pen several times, the horse has released his excess energy. He begins to realize that being driven away is boring and requires effort. Looking for an alternative to this routine, he starts watching the trainer. This is what the trainer is waiting for. The trainer changes his body language from an aggressive posture to an inviting posture. He stops and turns so he does not directly face the horse. He drops his arms to his side, inclines his head and his eyes down and slowly approaches the horse. As the trainer approaches, he offers an outstretched hand, much as a curious horse will stretch his neck and stick out his nose. The horse is intrigued by this invitation and allows the trainer to touch his forehead.

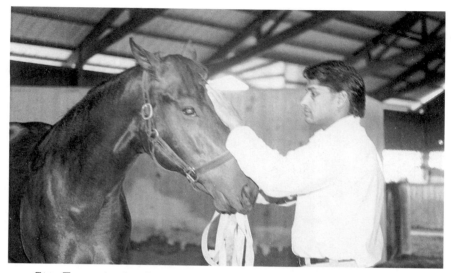

Step Four: Again, the trainer initiates a reassuring forehead rub. This time, the horse accepts. Note the expression on the horse's face as he absorbs the new idea. In his mind, the trainer has changed from adversary to friend. *(Photo courtesy of Suzie Oldham)*

Step Five: When the horse allows the trainer to rub his forehead, the trainer tests the relationship by walking 8 or 10 feet to one side or another. If the horse moves away, he is driven around again and the forehead rub is reinstated. When the horse follows the trainer, faces him and keeps his attention on the trainer, a turning point is reached. Held by an invisible line of trust, the horse is said to have "hooked up." After the horse has hooked up, the trainer can pick up the horse's feet without holding or restraining him in any way. The horse has made the decision that running away is unpleasant or boring and that facing and following the trainer is safe, interesting and rewarding. The horse's attitude has undergone a profound change. This change will make all subsequent training, such as bridling, saddling and riding, easier and safer than with conventional methods.

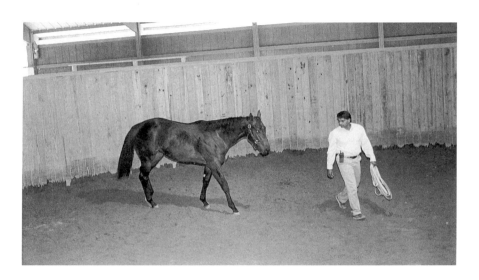

Step Five: The trainer turns and walks several feet to the right or left of the horse and the horse follows him. This horse has hooked up. He is being led with an invisible line of trust. Note the body language of the trainer: the oblique angle of his body and his downcast eyes say, "I am no threat, I am a friend."

(Photo courtesy of Suzie Oldham)

Hooking up is reached quickly with a skilled trainer. Since the trainer is speaking in body language which the horse understands instinctively, even wild or feral horses will respond to this method in a few hours. The average Thoroughbred or Standardbred yearling will hook up in 20 to 30 minutes. Hooking up normally marks the end of the first round pen session. (It is quite possible to go through all the steps below through breaking and riding on the first day in the round pen. This has been demonstrated many times at *Taylor Made*.)

Step Six: The hooked-up horse is calm and receptive. This is an ideal frame of mind for him to learn important lessons, such as allowing his feet to be picked up without any restraint, wearing the saddle pad and then the saddle with the girth tightened and moving under saddle.

The hooked-up horse is calm and receptive . . .

(Photo courtesy of Suzie Oldham)

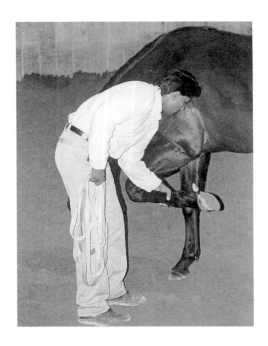

**. . . and surrenders his
feet to the trainer.**

*(Photo courtesy of
Suzie Oldham)*

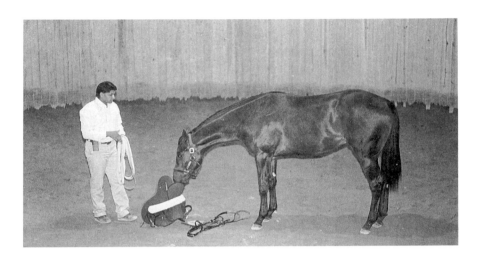

Step Six: When the horse has surrendered his feet to the trainer, the saddle, pad and bridle are brought into the ring. The horse is allowed to take his attention away from the trainer momentarily to look at these strange items. After he looks at and smells the tack, he hooks back up to the trainer. *(Photo courtesy of Suzie Oldham)*

The saddle pad is placed on the horse's back. After a moment to adjust to the pad, the trainer places the saddle on the horse. The girth is fastened on the right side, brought slowly under the belly and fastened on the left. All equipment is introduced and put on without holding or restraining the horse. The trainer's movements are slow and deliberate to avoid startling the horse. A forehead rub is given any time the horse appears apprehensive.

After the girth is tightened for the first time, the horse is driven away. At this point, he needs to become accustomed to the pressure of the girth which feels strange to him. Some yearlings will buck and jump while others only stiffen, but all horses must be made to move around the ring at this stage. Bucking could be the yearling's attempt to see if the saddle will come off. He needs to find out that it will not, at which point he hooks back up with the trainer. But bucking out of fear must be avoided. The apprehensive horse must be stopped and patted frequently to reinforce his confidence in the trainer. Keeping the horse's trust and attention enables the trainer to teach and the horse to retain the lesson.

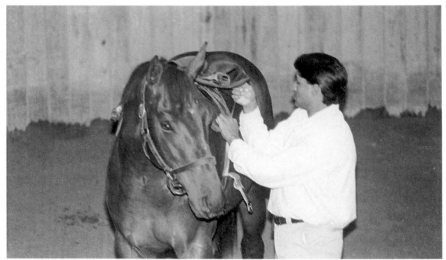

The horse is saddled and the girth tightened without restraint.

(Photo courtesy of Suzie Oldham)

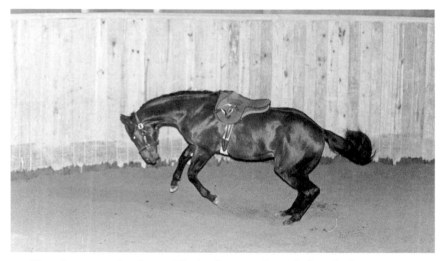

Freedom to resist the saddle in the round pen helps the horse understand and accept restraint. Allowing him to work this out helps prevent resistance later on in the training process.

(Photo courtesy of Suzie Oldham)

Throughout this process, the trainer's skill in reading the body language of the horse is paramount. When the young horse faces him, he must recognize by the horse's stance and expression if the horse is looking for reassurance. A worried horse has a tentative look about him and the muscles above the eyes have a characteristic look of tension. His ears may move forward and back, showing apprehension and indecision. The trainer will understand this body language and rub the horse's forehead to reassure him. The trainer then walks away and the horse follows. The horse receives another forehead rub which further encourages him and reinforces the hooking up.

The playful, cocky youngster wears a different expression. He may appear tense, but it is from high spirits, not apprehension. His eyes will look bright and keen, without the tension above them of the more timid horse. His ears may prick sharply, showing his confidence and alertness. This youngster may need to be driven around the pen a few more times to vent his playfulness and return his attention to the trainer and the lessons.

Step Seven: The bridle is introduced quietly to the horse. Holding the headstall in one hand, the trainer holds the bit against the horse's mouth until he opens it. The bit is never forced into the horse's mouth and the headstall slips on much like the youngster's halter. A mild, rubber-covered snaffle is used to protect the young horse's mouth.

Step Eight: When the horse accepts the sensation of the saddle and bridle, the stirrups are let down and long lines run through them to the bit. The trainer then drives the horse around the pen, stopping, changing direction and regulating the pace with the long lines and his body language. When the horse understands the long lines and allows himself to be stopped, steered and directed, he is ready to be mounted and ridden.

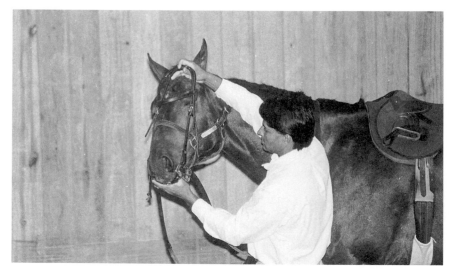

Step Seven: The bridle is introduced gently. The rubber-covered bit is never forced into the horse's mouth.
(Photo courtesy of Suzie Oldham)

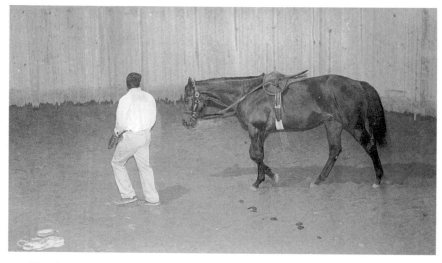

The horse accepts the saddle and bridle and again hooks up with the trainer.
(Photo courtesy of Suzie Oldham)

Step Eight: Ground-driving the horse teaches him to stop and turn from the pressure of the bit. Round pen training is so effective that most yearlings progress from the initial hooking up on the first day to being ground-driven around the pen on the third day. Older yearlings begin to be ridden at this point. For demonstration purposes, some horses are ridden in the initial session.

(Photo courtesy of Suzie Oldham)

Sales yearlings are brought through the ground-driving stage in the round pen, but they are not ridden before the sale. At this point, round pen work is reduced to two or three brief sessions a week of conditioning rather than training. The yearlings are not driven, but are free-lunged in the round pen to improve their fitness level. After the sale, the saddling, bridling and ground-driving are resumed. Having learned these lessons without pain or fear the first time, the yearlings accept these restraints readily. Mounting and riding are only more steps in the process that the yearling has learned to accept. Within a week or so, all the yearlings are being ridden outside around the paddocks.

Round pen training is safe and effective because it lets the individual horse dictate how fast to move through the program. Beyond the initial hooking up session, each lesson is kept to only 15 or 20 minutes to avoid tiring or stressing horse. Some yearlings need three or four days to absorb new lessons while others learn the entire program on the first or second day. The yearling that is bright and interested may proceed to the next step, while the submissive youngster that stands with a lowered head and shows little curiosity has had enough for one day. The step by step approach of round pen training allows the trainer to gauge the readiness of the horse at each stage and to make the correct decision.

After three years of using the round pen method to break hundreds of yearlings, we have concluded that it is the safest and easiest method. A horse that is unafraid and responding of his own free will benefits in three ways: (1) The horse is less prone to injure himself because he is not reacting out of panic or fear; (2) the horse does not suffer the ill effects of stress, a common side effect of conventional training that uses force and restraint; and, (3) the horse remembers the lessons because all progress results from his own conscious decisions. This is a radical departure from conventional methods, where a nervous young horse preoccupied with his own safety, is restrained and ridden without understanding why or how to respond. Since we adopted the round pen method, we have seen the incidence of horse and rider injuries fall to practically zero. Following up on these yearlings, we receive reports from trainers that round pen trained horses are easier to handle, train better and suffer fewer injuries at the track.

While I do not advise you to build a round pen and start running your yearlings around it after reading this description, I recommend you locate a trainer who has these skills. They are not difficult to learn, but the body language of the trainer must be seen to be understood. The reactions of horse in the round pen must be interpreted by someone who has a thorough understanding of the process. An expert round pen trainer could be hired as a consultant until your staff acquires the skills to use these techniques. I urge you to investigate this method of training and consider making this investment.

Prepping Sales Yearlings: Top prices are gained only from well-prepared yearlings. While pedigree and conformation cannot be changed, the advantage gained with proper preparation can often be measured in hundreds or even thousands of dollars at the sale.

Preparation begins a minimum of 80 to 100 days before the sale. Yearlings that are to be sold in July are brought in from the pastures in April to begin being fitted physically, mentally and finally, cosmetically.

Daily Care: Yearlings that are destined for the summer and fall sales spend their days in the barn and are turned out into paddocks at night. Fillies may share a paddock, but separate the colts. Keeping one colt to a paddock minimizes the bumps and scrapes that two young males will inflict on one another. Night turnout is preferable because it is cooler and the yearlings' coats are maintained in a better condition if they can avoid the summer sun and biting insects. When they are brought inside in the morning, they are checked thoroughly for sprains, cuts or abrasions. The feet are picked out and any missing or sprung shoes reported to the manager. After any exercise or conditioning work, the feet are checked again.

Stabling sales yearlings during the day has several benefits. Because they will eat all their meals in their stalls, you can adjust the amounts fed and maintain precise weights. Sleep is very important for the young horses' growth. Yearlings fed inside have more opportunities to nap after eating. Schedule quiet periods each day to allow the yearlings to rest undisturbed.

Yearlings wear both halters and neckstraps at all times. Each halter and neckstrap has the horse's name on it. If the halter is lost, a temporary one is used and the horse's name written on a piece of tape fastened to the halter. Adjust the halters so buckles are level on both sides. Before the horse is shipped or presented, oil the halter and shine the brass. Cotton flannel wrapped around a clean, gleaming halter before shipping shows a professional attention to detail.

Exercising the Yearling to Build Muscle and Bone: Conditioning the sales yearling is necessary to develop the muscle tone and size that buyers expect to see in a potential racehorse. It is also necessary to compensate for the artificially controlled life we impose on the young horse. Since we have removed the colt from the pasture and his playmates, he is not getting the benefit of galloping and horseplay with his companions. We must replace this natural form of conditioning with controlled exercise. At *Taylor Made*, we use a three-step program of round pen work, treadmill work and hand-walking for developing yearlings. The program is on a five-day schedule of four days of conditioning followed by one day off. The three types of conditioning tools offer different benefits and are blended to suit the individual horse.

Before any conditioning program is initiated, two evaluations are done. First, the colt is examined to determine what sort of conditioning will produce the optimum result. All yearlings vary in body type. Some are lean and spare and will benefit from treadmill workouts that build muscle and bulk. Others have an abundance of muscle and perhaps some fat. Such colts need more round pen work to develop hardness and stamina. Within each type of program is each horse's individual tolerance for work which must be taken into account. The goal is to challenge and develop the young horse without stressing him.

Hand-walking is the cornerstone of the yearling's basic training. It would be hard to find a more natural form of exercise than walking. Hand-walking conditions the yearling gently and it teaches the manners that make all other programs feasible. All conditioning work, whether it is round pen, treadmill or hand-walking, demand a relaxed, receptive horse to be safe and effective. A yearling that doesn't understand "whoa" or hasn't had enough training to tolerate a lunge line touching his hocks is not ready for round pen conditioning. Putting an insecure yearling on the treadmill is asking for a wreck. Hand-walking teaches colts and fillies to lead well, stand quietly and have confidence in the handler, all of which help the horse show well at the sale. Time spent hand-walking the young horse will be repaid in fewer injuries and more interest from the buyers.

Yearlings are hand-walked along the lanes around and between the paddocks. Each route takes the groom and his horse back to the barn, where he practices setting up and showing the yearling. After a few minutes of rehearsal for potential buyers, they go off around the paddock again. This is done every fourth day and the distance is increased gradually until the grooms and their yearlings are walking three miles a day.

Round pen conditioning differs from round pen training. Round pen *training* introduces the yearling to new ideas. There are frequent breaks in the work and the sessions proceed until the lesson is learned, usually about 20 to 30 minutes. Round pen *conditioning* means to drive the horse at a trot or gallop both ways around the round pen to make him fit. These sessions begin gradually and are of short duration. The first time in the round pen is limited to two or three minutes. Add a couple of minutes each session until the colt is spending eight to 12 minutes working in the round pen. A colt that is overweight might be eased up to 15 minutes of work. Because round pen work is beneficial for taking weight off a horse, a yearling that is too heavy may spend three days a week in the round pen. A horse that needs more weight might use the round pen only once a week or less.

Treadmill work is slow, intense work and is excellent for adding muscle and bulk. It may be used every fourth day for yearlings that thrive on it and less for others. Introduce treadmill work slowly. There is always the possibility of frightening or injuring a yearling on the treadmill. Spend the first two or three days simply walking the colt onto and off of the treadmill. When he is comfortable with the looks of the machine and the feel of the belt under his hooves, turn it on at the slowest setting. Let the colt become familiar with the feel of the treadmill belt starting and stopping. After the yearling learns to walk with the motion and is relaxed with its operations, set the machine at a fast walk for three or four minutes. Increase the session gradually, adding one minute each time until the colt walks eight to 10 minutes per treadmill session. Eight to 10 minutes doesn't sound like much exercise, but treadmill work requires a lot of exertion and can be stressful. Always stop the session early if the colt becomes tired.

With any type of conditioning, the guiding principle is to do less work than the yearling is capable of, always stopping short of an all-out effort. End the session before the horse is sweaty and blowing hard since a tired colt may easily put a foot wrong and hurt himself. Young bones and joints are easily injured, so it is imperative to avoid fatigue when conditioning the yearling.

Grooming: Sales yearlings are groomed immaculately for months, not just weeks, before the sale. The lustrous patina of a healthy, well-groomed yearling cannot be achieved with any hair polish and last-minute efforts. It requires daily grooming.

Effective grooming requires five tools: 1) A rubber grooming mitt or a soft rubber curry comb and a shedding tool during the spring; 2) a water brush, which is a stiff, rice roots brush for bringing the dirt and dander up out of the coat and for brushing the mane and tail; 3) a soft body brush for bringing the oil out and making the coat shine; 4) a rub rag for drying the horse after a bath, for removing dust and adding shine, and for rubbing the legs and joints to aid circulation (a good rub rag is made of heavy woven cloth, like burlap); and 5) a hoof pick.

Begin the daily grooming by rubbing the coat with the rubber glove or curry. Clean the curry frequently by knocking it against the back of the stiff water brush. After the rubber glove or curry, use the water brush to remove the dirt raised by the curry. Wet the water brush and brush the mane and tail, gently removing any tangles or pieces of straw. Moistening the mane with water and brushing it will train it to lay on the right side. Then all loose hair and dirt are vacuumed up. Feet are picked and oiled with baby oil daily. Don't neglect the heel area. Dry heels look unattractive and the area must be checked daily for cuts, abrasions or scratches that need furacin salve. For presentation, apply hoof oil to the feet and baby oil around the eyes and muzzle. This routine will take at least 30 minutes to complete.

Grooming tools must be kept clean - they should remove dirt, not redistribute it. Disinfect all brushes every second day. Separate brushes and disposable rubber gloves are used for any horse with a skin disease. The vacuum cleaner needs to be emptied at least once a week, more often when the horses are shedding.

The grooming routine varies with the conditioning schedule. The routine described above is followed on the yearling's day off from work. On round pen or treadmill days, the yearling is brushed quickly with the water brush to knock off any dirt or mud. The feet are picked clean, then he is taken out for his workout. After the work session, the yearling is bathed and the groom dries him with the rub rag, paying particular attention to rubbing the knees, hocks and fetlocks. Then he is thoroughly groomed. Extra time is spent using the soft body brush to bring out the shine, followed by a final polish with the rag.

The groom's job is made easier if the stalls are always clean and well-bedded. The manure is removed regularly so the horses cannot lay down in it. A firm cushion of bedding prevents the horses from scraping their hocks. To prevent the yearlings from rubbing and breaking mane and tail hairs, remove all feed tubs after they are finished eating.

Sales yearlings do not wear blankets as a rule. But yearlings which are sold privately after the fall sales may wear blankets in cold weather. Blankets help to keep them clean and make their coats lay down flat and smooth, which increases the shine. All blankets are tagged with the horses' names (dam's name with year of birth) written on duct tape. Blankets must fit over the rump so they don't slide off to one side and they must not be tight over the withers. Check the withers, shoulders and chest for broken hairs, which indicate that the blanket is too tight or is rubbing. Belly straps must be snug underneath the stomach to avoid movement and cross over at the center point. If the horses were turned out wearing blankets, remove them daily to check for injuries, then replace them.

Shoeing: Most yearlings are shod for the sales to keep their feet in good shape and to give the best presentation. They are shod in front only, using regular racing plates with no tips or caulks. Have the farrier shoe the yearling for the first time about six weeks before the sale. One week prior to the sale, have him reset the shoes. If the colt has a hot nail, you have time to correct it. Follow this schedule and the yearling's feet will be perfect for the sales.

Polish and Presentation: Presenting sales yearlings to buyers visiting the farm is an important part of the business. How well your yearlings and employees perform at such outings can make the difference between making a profit and showing a loss. Since a properly prepared yearling brings many more dollars at the auction than a "backyard" yearling of comparable breeding and quality, proper care and management of these young horses is vital.

Before showing yearlings, make sure the barn reflects the quality of its horses. Have the aisles swept, windows washed and flower beds tended. All empty buckets go to the back of the barn, out of the show area.

Grooms' and handlers' appearances must reflect high standards. Clean clothes in good condition and good grooming are essential. Young men should have their hair and beards trimmed. Young ladies with long hair should tie it back. All shirttails are tucked in, all shoes are clean and all fingernails scrubbed. Matching jackets or polo shirts in your colors are a nice touch, but optional. White shirts and dark trousers are an affordable alternative.

Presentation: Every young horse must learn to pose properly for presentation. This is vital for sales yearlings - buyers have only pedigree and appearance to go on. The pedigree cannot be changed. Consequently, the yearling's appearance must make the most favorable impression possible. Even the best-conformed horse may look awkward or unbalanced if he is not standing with "a leg on each corner."

The proper pose sets up the horse for viewing from the side. The front and hind legs must be placed apart enough so all four legs are visible at the same time. The front and hind pairs of legs should appear to bear an equal amount of weight. The horse should not lean over his front end or rock back on his hindquarters, both of which make him look unbalanced. The front legs should not be so far apart that the horse appears to point a front foot or stand with one front leg under his belly. The hind legs must be close enough together so the hindquarters don't look flat due to an extended hind leg. The neck should be in a position that looks natural, but alert. If the head and neck are too high, it makes the topline look weak. Too low a neck looks "sleepy" and throws too much weight onto the front end. The right attitude for the horse's neck is where he appears the most balanced.

The well-trained yearling that walks in a straight line and halts to assume the position described above looks completely natural. Hours of patient work, practice and correction have gone into this seemingly effortless demonstration. Horses, like people, often assume a characteristic posture that is not flattering. It may take hundreds of small corrections and adjustments to teach a colt to place his hind feet slightly apart and not to rest one hind leg. Many hours will be spent teaching a curious yearling to stand quietly and not to lean over his front legs toward his handler. All this must be practiced and perfected until it is second nature for the colt or filly to stop on cue, place his feet and stand properly.

Horses accustomed to working on stone chips will walk differently and stand differently on grass and vice versa. Provide areas of both surfaces on which to practice. European buyers often request to see a yearling walked on the grass and a yearling that is not prepared for this will not show well. Time spent on the finer details of presentation will be justified at the sale.

As the sales grow close, designate certain off-days as "show days" for groups of buyers who visit the farm. During specified hours in the afternoon, have the yearlings taken out, walked and set up for inspection. These are valuable practice sessions before the sale. While in their familiar surroundings, the yearlings can become accustomed to the confusion of large groups of people and to strangers approaching and touching them. The grooms get an idea how their yearlings will react at the sale as they polish their showmanship skills.

As the crop of yearlings are prepared for the sale, you may notice that some young horses show better for certain grooms than they do for others. When a colt stands quietly and walks off straight for one particular handler, you have found compatible personalities. Your goal is to find compatible pairs of yearlings and grooms. But this works both ways - sometimes, a yearling that always showed well for a certain groom will change. The colt that fidgets and act ups for his familiar handler needs a different hand on the shank. Usually these yearlings will stop misbehaving and pay attention when a new groom shows them. The unfamiliar hand and voice keep the colt's respectful interest. Be prepared to make these changes, even at the sale. The sale is the point of all your careful preparation - be alert to whatever will improve the way the yearling is presented.

Choose your equipment well in advance of the sale. Yearlings may be shown in halters with Chifney bits or in bridles. Lead shanks should be leather, with or without chains. One kind works as well as the other. It looks best if all your horses wear the same equipment, so choose one or the other. I prefer bridles because they look professional, they show the horse's head to best advantage and they offer the most control. If your yearlings are to wear bridles, allow 30 days for them to become accustomed to them. If you are not able to allow enough time to educate the yearlings to bridles, stay with halters and Chifney bits.

Setting a Reserve: As the yearling is prepared and conditioned in the weeks before the sale, you naturally will evaluate the animal and attempt to predict its selling price. Since the sale is the culmination of at least two years of planning and considerable financial investment, this is an irresistible exercise. But if you plan to set a reserve price for the yearling, such speculation becomes more serious. Use the time before the sale to determine a figure that best serves *your* interests. By setting a reserve, you are saying, in effect, below this dollar amount the bidders' judgment is flawed - the yearling is worth the reserve price (or more) and I will be further by ahead keeping him. The key to setting a realistic reserve lies the question, am I prepared to be in the racing business?

Setting a realistic reserve price begins with establishing a base price, then adjusting it to reflect changes that occur in the market. The prices of the sire's get, the mare's previous offspring, and the yearling itself form the basis for determining value. How good an individual is he - does he have better conformation than his siblings or does he have more flaws? Has he experienced any setbacks in growth and development that are not of lasting importance but may detract from his value? Most important to establishing a base value are the racing records compiled by other horses in the yearling's family.

With a base price established, look for factors that may cause you to adjust that price. Again, race records are pivotal - a half-brother's recent placing in a stakes race will boost the yearling's value immediately. Recent racetrack performance by close relatives should be taken into consideration when evaluating the yearling. Even work-out times of related horses in training may be significant. Continue to monitor selling prices during the sale to keep your assessment current.

This process takes a lot of background information and even more research. Doing a thorough job may require more time than you have to devote to the project. Add to this the difficulty of being completely objective and detached about your yearling. Setting a reserve price for your horse is as difficult as pricing your home to sell. Unless you are in the real estate business, it is almost impossible to know all the factors that can affect its value and price. I recommend you get some help with this project.

A qualified appraiser can help you evaluate your yearlings objectively and with the highest degree of accuracy possible. An appraiser sees thousands of yearlings before and as they pass through the sales ring. He has access to all the facts pertinent to your yearling's potential market value. His eye for quality and the lack of a financial stake in the selling price of your yearling allows him to give an objective appraisal.

Other sources of help with appraising your yearlings for setting reserves are fellow breeders, farm managers and bloodstock agents. Gather as many qualified opinions as possible before setting your reserve. Do not expect their judgments to be in agreement - they will vary and you will be left to reconcile the differences. The more thought put into the decision, the better prepared you will be to either accept the highest bid or to take him home.

At the Sale: Yearlings should arrive at the sales grounds four days before the sale. This gives them time to settle in and become accustomed to different sights and surroundings. And the grooms need time to bath and polish the yearlings and to practice showing them before the buyers arrive. Schedule your grooms so that one person remains in your stabling area overnight. Someone should always be on duty in case of a colic, a cast horse or any other emergency.

Change the yearlings' routine as little as possible. Have a supply of your own hay and grain at the sale grounds before the yearlings arrive. Don't make them adjust to a different diet. Feed them at the same hours they were accustomed to at home.

Yearlings should be hand-walked each day for an hour before daylight. This quiet period of gentle exercise will help to settle them for the stressful days that follow. Each yearling may be taken out and shown 50 or more times a day. The morning walk helps to offset this kind of pressure on the young horses.

Grooming at the sales is the same thorough routine as at the farm with a few extra touches added. A small amount of coat polish is useful for enhancing the gloss and repelling stains. White markings are scrubbed clean before the sale and maintained pristine white by rubbing a little talc or cornstarch into the hair. The hooves are cleaned and a little Hooflex or fish oil is rubbed into the wall. A small amount of oil is better than a lot because it attracts less dust. The skin around the eyes and on the muzzle can be moistened with baby oil. Again, apply it sparingly. A bleached or faded mane may be restored to its natural shade with a little ladies hair coloring.

While the sale is under way, show the yearling to as many people as possible, particularly if the horse is not one of the top yearlings in the sale. Know the yearling's pedigree *thoroughly*. Be prepared to quote sales prices and the latest racing results for all the best representatives of the yearling's family. Every sale has a few "stars," but the majority of yearlings will bring more money if promoted.

A good example of this is the well-bred colt that has a conformation flaw. Because of a physical imperfection, this colt will not be looked at by the upper echelon of buyers, pedigree not withstanding. However, there is a large class of buyers with financial limitations. These buyers may note the horse's fine pedigree and conclude that they cannot afford the horse. Not bothering to look at the colt before the sale, they don't bid and lose the opportunity to acquire a well-bred runner. The market was there, but lack of promotion kept the yearling and the buyer apart.

A lot of effort goes into teaching a yearling to show well.

(Photo courtesy of Joy Gilbert)

But extra effort is rewarded at the sale.

(Photo courtesy of Suzie Oldham)

This illustrates the need to show the sales yearling to as many buyers as possible. You cannot always tell the serious buyers from the "tire-kickers" and some buyers have friends or scouts looking for them. Do not rule out anyone as a potential buyer. The larger the number of showings, the better the chance of getting a good price for the horse.

Prepping Racing Yearlings: Yearlings that are intended for racing only and not for the sales enjoy a few more months of carefree youth than their counterparts. Spring is spent out in the pasture in groups of like sexes. During the hot summer months, they are stabled during the day and turned out at night to avoid the heat and flies. They are groomed and trained to lead and stand, but less frequently than sales yearlings. While their health, growth and condition is monitored as carefully that of the sales yearlings, they experience less pressure.

In September or October, childhood ends for racing yearlings, too. A gradual transition in their routine begins that prepares them for training. They are turned out individually and groomed and handled more intensively. They get their first set of shoes. Round pen work is introduced and the yearlings go through all the stages of hooking up, surrendering the feet, saddling and ground-driving, as I described earlier for sales yearlings.

Unlike sales yearlings, the round pen education continues for racing yearlings. Ground-driven until they become bridle-wise, they are bellied, then mounted and ridden in preparation for the training track and, finally, the racetrack.

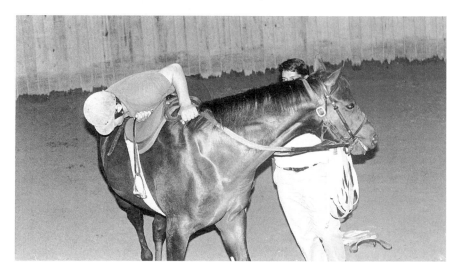

Racing yearlings receive the same basic round pen training as sales yearlings. Later, they are broken to ride. Bellying the yearling is the first step . . . *(Photo courtesy of Suzie Oldham)*

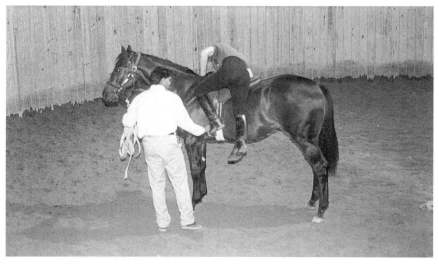

. . . followed shortly by mounting. *(Photo courtesy of Suzie Oldham)*

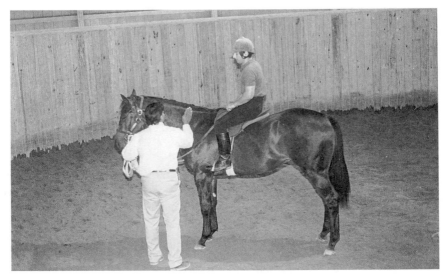

This yearling has never been mounted before, yet he remains quiet.
(Photo courtesy of Suzie Oldham)

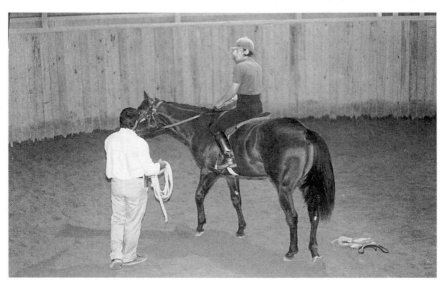

The rider encourages him to walk on as the trainer steps back to reinforce the rider's efforts. *(Photo courtesy of Suzie Oldham)*

Note the trainer's posture as he helps to send the yearling forward - the same used during the earlier lessons.

(Photo courtesy of Suzie Oldham)

Day three under saddle for this colt. He can carry his rider around the round pen at all three gaits, in both directions. In a few days he will be trotting figure-eights around the paddock outside like a schooled horse.

(Photo courtesy of Suzie Oldham)

The colt walks calmly outside to be schooled in the fresh air. Weeks ahead of conventionally started colts, he is confident and mentally prepared for his career on the racetrack.

(Photo courtesy of Suzie Oldham)

Chapter 12

Stallion Management

Stallions are judged more critically and culled more extensively than broodmares. A broodmare is purchased and bred. After one or two foals, you will decide whether to keep her because she produced good foals or to cull her because her foals were crooked or otherwise not up to her quality. It's a simple decision which is part of the business of owning broodmares. It is not as easy to cut your losses and move on with a stallion. A stallion has the ability to produce 40 of those slow, crooked, embarrassing foals in one year. In three years, everyone will know they lack talent as well as looks.

The odds against a stallion becoming a top sire are great. Only one in four stallions will even survive as a sire past the 11th year. The other three will be sold at a discount, probably to breeders of jumpers, stock horses and other non-racing interests.

Finding Stallions to Stand: The standard for selecting a stallion to stand has two parts:
(1) The stallion must be a horse that the public recognizes. Trying to promote an obscure horse in a sophisticated market is futile. The magnificent specimen with neither a race record nor a pedigree is not a stallion prospect.
(2) The horse must have demonstrated racing ability. He must have shown talent on the racetrack to merit a chance to reproduce himself. You - and the owners of the mares you hope to get - are breeding to produce racehorses. Not every top sire was a champion racehorse. But most showed talent on the racetrack. A fashionably bred horse with a case of the slows is a poor candidate to sire winners. Look up from that fine pedigree - can you see the finish line?

257

A talented racehorse that was injured early in his career will be tough, but not impossible to promote if he has a strong pedigree. If he showed racing talent, it's reasonable to gamble that he has good genes, too.

Making a Stallion into a Sire: "A stallion's reputation is made on other people's mares." I've repeated this old adage before and it should be memorized by anyone who wants to establish a stallion as a sire. A stallion's potential for siring runners can be realized only with good quality mares. Not even a classic sire can produce much from a band of low-quality mares. The success of any stallion will depend in large measure on the quality of the mares he covers. Your task, then, is to *get your stallion the right mares.*

The best mares for an unproven stallion are young, good-looking mares with good racetrack records and racing performance in their pedigrees. Young mares are good choices because they are *potential producers of top racehorses.* Select young racemares which are free of the conformational defects that yearling buyers dislike, such as calf knees. Your goal is to produce runners, but these foals must first pass through the sales rings. No one has rolled these dice yet and the possibility exists that they will come up as big winners. Bear in mind that yearling buyers are buying on potential, not demonstrated past performance.

Load the dice with racing ability to improve your chances. A crop of racetrack failures will ruin your horse very quickly. Maximize every opportunity to produce a runner by choosing *mares with racing talent* and some depth of pedigree.

Promotion: Getting the right mares is a two part strategy. First, you must attract mare owners to your stallion through promotional activities. Second, you must convince them to book to your stallion by setting the stud fee at the right price.

Advertising your stallion is essential. Professionally prepared advertisements, brochures, press releases and other materials are needed to generate enthusiasm. There are a number of advertising agencies that specialize in stallion promotion. Seek their help.

Promotional tactics for the stallion's first year at stud must, by necessity, emphasize his race record and pedigree. A win photo is a great advertisement. If he won or placed in good company, mention the other horses in the race. Winning times are valuable advertising if they are good times. Pedigree is a valuable tool for promoting the horse if he has a distinguished family or relatives that are winning on the track. Both the race record and the pedigree must be cast in the light of potential. Your stallion has demonstrated racing ability and he has the right family. Crossed with the right mares, he has the *potential to sire the next world-beater*. For the first-year stallion, this is not hype, it's the absolute truth. Until it's been proven otherwise, you may have the next Mr. Prospector. Promote the promise in your young stallion.

Advertising materials are only tools and must be backed up with personal, knowledgeable and enthusiastic promotional efforts. A marketing person must work full-time to fill your stallion's book with quality mares. This marketing person must make person-to-person contact with people who will make breeding decisions or who can influence them. He must have the energy and enthusiasm that says, "This stallion is going to make a name for himself and for those who breed to him. We're going places - come join us." Bloodstock agents are a rich source of referrals. They must be contacted regularly and reminded of everything of note about your stallion. Trainers and their owners have race mares retiring from the track. They must be made aware of your horse and approached for possible bookings. New people in the business represent an opportunity to help establish your stallion. Promotional efforts that are also educational for the newcomer are the best kind of public relations.

After the first breeding season, expand your tactics. Advertise that your horse stood for this much money and bred 40 mares with a conception rate of 90%. A list of well-bred, quality mares that were bred to your horse is an excellent advertising tool. It is not necessary to name the mares' owners. Good mares will speak for themselves. Have photos of good-looking weanlings in your ads. Conformationally correct weanlings suggest that the stallion's get will bring good prices at the yearling sales. Your promotional efforts must generate excitement for your stallion's yearlings. If a weanling has sold for a good price, publish it to add momentum. As the sales approach, feature photos of your horse's best yearlings in your ads. Promote the combination of looks, a young sire and a good race mare. Keep records of where and for what price these yearlings were sold. Nothing recommends a stallion more than yearlings that sell for three to five times the stud fee. Mare owners who are happy with their breeding decisions will book their mares to your stallion again. Their success inspires other owners to book to your horse. Keep improving the quality of your stallion's book.

By the fourth and fifth years, the stallion's first two crops will be in training and racing. Know where they are and follow their careers. Know who is training them and how they're working, right down to the fractions. You need information on the performance of your stallion's get to promote him. Respectable time over distance at any recognized racetrack, from Nebraska to New Zealand, is a credit to your horse.

After the fifth year, the stallion must promote himself. If you have filled his book with good mares, his offspring will be making a name for him. But if he has no offspring which sold for high prices, few horses on the track and fewer winners, he's a hard horse to promote. Now is the time to consider culling this horse and replacing him.

Pricing Seasons: Establishing the right price for the young stallion's seasons is an important tool for attracting quality mares. Owners of quality broodmares expect to pay a fair price for a season from a top young horse. They also hope to make a profit from their investment. Give them the chance to do both and you will fill your stallion's book. The price that enables you to select mares that will make your horse is what I call the "popular price." Establishing a popular price is as important as promoting the horse. It's a strategy that works from the first year, right on through until the horse is made.

The right price for a young stallion's season is a price that attracts more potential breedings than there are openings in his book. You must be able to select mares that will help establish your horse and reject those that won't. Look past the immediate gain of the stud fee and focus on the racetrack. Is this mare likely to produce a runner? If so, she belongs in your stallion's book at whatever price will convince her owner to breed to your stallion.

The day your stallion has his first stakes winner is a happy occasion. Work will stop momentarily as the good news goes around the farm. Champagne will flow and you will be tempted to raise the price of his season. Don't do it.

Raising the price of the season fee too soon has two risks. It could cause you to lose the quality mares that are making your stallion. Mare owners may not remain loyal to your stallion until the next big winner, deciding instead that your horse was a "flash in the pan." The second risk in raising a stallion's stud fee prematurely is that it may require you to adjust it downward sometime later. Having to lower the price of a stallion's season can be a disaster. Mare owners will stay away in droves, thinking that your horse is on the way down. This becomes a self-fulfilling prophecy. Don't fall into the trap of raising the price of the season too soon. The mare owners who helped you establish your horse are still valued clients. Keep them happy. Keep them loyal to your stallion and you will continue to get the high-quality mares that make your stallion's reputation. If you have investors who push you to make more money with the stallion, book 10 extra mares of the highest quality possible. This will raise money and keep everybody happy.

Stallion Facilities: Stallions require strong, safe stalls and paddocks. The stallion barn must accommodate the special needs of the stallion while it impresses potential customers. A facility of quality and beauty suggests the value of its occupants and the stallion barn becomes part of your promotion. Stallions also require a staff of the highest calibre. Qualified stallion personnel are professionals whose wages reflect advanced training and horsemanship skills. All this represents an investment beyond that of the purchase price of the horse. The owner of one or two stallions may find it easier and more profitable to board his stallions. A farm specializing in standing stallions will offer a superior staff in a prestigious atmosphere. Boarding your stallion at a premier stallion facility that has high standards protects your investment. And, standing your horse at a "Park Avenue" address may be your first step in promoting him.

Exercise: The stallion is the most neglected horse on many farms. One of his most basic needs - exercise - is frequently ignored.

Most stallions are turned out for only three or four hours a day. Stallion managers find it convenient to keep the horse in his stall most of the time, rather than to go out to the paddock and bring him inside for each cover. This results in a stale, disinterested stallion. The stallion owner usually pays the price for this lack of exercise in fewer and fewer mares settled each year.

A stallion needs lots of exercise to remain sharp and interested in courting and breeding his mares. He should be outside more than he's inside. The more exercise he has, the better his condition and the better his mares look to him. A stallion that is kept outside more than he's kept inside will usually keep fit by running and playing. The fresh air, the grass, the sunshine and the sight of another stallion in an adjacent paddock stimulates him. A properly managed stallion remains fit, fresh and interested in his mares well into his 20s.

A stallion should go outside after his morning feed and remain there until he's needed for breeding. After the cover, he should go back outside until the next meal or breeding, whichever comes first. After the 4:00 p.m. feed, put him back outside until 9:00 p.m. or so. It's often necessary to rearrange the schedules of some employees to accomplish this, but it's worth the trouble. Leave the stallion outside as much as possible.

The only time a stallion should not be turned out is when he is hungry and the pasture is lush. Don't confuse a hungry stallion with a good eater that seems hungry all the time. Hungry means empty. A horse that hasn't eaten for five hours is hungry and if you turn him out on lush pasture you are inviting problems. Offer him a flake of hay 30 minutes before turnout. Keeping a supply of good timothy hay in his stall discourages him from gorging on lush grass and becoming ill.

Occasionally a stallion won't exercise himself in the paddock. In such cases, he must be worked in the round pen, lunged or put on a treadmill. Some farms ride their stallions and that's a good policy. But I think the round pen is even better and safer for exercising stallions. All sound stallions benefit from moderate work in the round pen. Ten to 15 minutes a day will keep the horse in good condition. The only stallions that should not go in the round pen or receive any type of forced exercise are those with injuries or arthritic conditions that would be worsened by work.

Turnout Facilities: The stallion paddock must be large - three to five acres - with good footing everywhere. Put stone dust or tanbark around the gates and over any slippery spots. Stallions play hard and a fall could cost you a season. I discussed the building of paddocks in Chapter Three.

Stallion paddocks should be clustered together but segregated from all other horses. It's natural for a stallion to see the other stallions nearby, but the sight of mares or even a riding horse will make him fret and run the fence. Fifty feet is the minimum safe distance between stallions and all other types of horses. Put a hedge or a screen of trees between stallions and other horses.

Stallion paddocks have high, strong fences which allow the horses to see each other but keep them safely apart. Note the screen of trees and vegetation on the left which separates the stallions from all other horses on the farm. *(Photo courtesy of Martin Pierce)*

Paddock assignments depend on which horses get along and which do not. Most stallions enjoy the sight of the horse in the next paddock but a few absolutely hate each other. They don't need a reason, they simply hate the sight and smell of each other. An angry stallion will fret and run the fence line until he loses condition. Separate these stallions by moving one to another paddock to relieve the stress on both. Or, find a "neutral" stallion that is tolerated by both and put the neutral horse in the paddock between the feuding pair. If you are able to separate them by more than one paddock, all the better. You cannot change this behavior. You must work around it.

Overweight Stallions - a Common Management Error: Too often, stallions are allowed to become overweight. They are over-fed and kept inside almost all of the time and they suffer the consequences. It is not unusual to see horses 12 or 14 years old that appear to be 20 or 22. Some even develop a potbelly and resemble pregnant broodmares. Overweight stallions frequently lose interest in their mares and suffer from lameness and other debilitating effects of premature aging. This is preventable with good stallion management.

Many stallions gain weight during the off season and lose weight during the breeding season. Avoid this problem by weighing the stallion every month. Establish an ideal weight and feed him to that weight. By weighing the horse monthly, you will note small gains or losses that your eye cannot detect. The horse's feed and exercise regimens can be adjusted before the horse suffers any effects from too much or too little weight.

Grooming, Blanketing, Lights: Stallions need to be groomed every day, not only for appearance, but for the horse's health and temperament as well. Daily grooming allows the stallion to be inspected for injuries or other health problems. Grooming reminds the stallion of his manners and teaches him that he's not going to the breeding shed every time someone walks into his stall. Grooming should be done by the stallion's regular groom. The same man who cares for and brushes a stallion every day will know immediately if something is wrong with his horse.

It's not necessary to blanket a stallion. A horse that is groomed and turned out every day develops a good, thick coat for the winter. It adjusts to varying temperatures and provides good insulation. The only time a horse's winter coat is inadequate is in cold or freezing rain. Bring the stallion inside before he gets wet and chilled.

I believe in keeping stallions under lights in similar fashion to what is done with mares and for the same reason. It's natural for the stallion to breed in April or May, not in February. If you manage him properly, priming his system for breeding with the use of lights, you'll be more successful in the breeding shed in February and March. When you start keeping broodmares under lights in December, do the same with the stallions. Your stallions will benefit from the Lights Program just as your mares do.

Preparation - Making Sure the Mare is Ready: In the wild, horses live in herds comprised of one stallion and several mares. Each mare is receptive to breeding only a few days every three or four weeks. Her willingness to stand for the stallion usually coincides with ovulation, which may be nature's way of aiding conception. Within the herd, each mare's cycle is timed a bit differently. To breed all mares during the season, the stallion must be ready to breed at any time. It is much the same with our domesticated Thoroughbreds and Standardbreds - reproduction takes place only when the mare accepts the stallion and she is able to conceive. While a well-managed stallion is always ready, domesticated mares are the "wild card" in the breeding process. Their behavior can be extremely unpredictable. It requires the veterinarian, the teaser, the teasing man and the stallion manager's staff to all work in concert to ensure that the mare is truly ready to be bred.

The Stallion Farm Veterinarian: A breeding complex requires the services of a veterinarian specializing in reproduction. When the mares arrive to be bred, the veterinarian is on hand to examine and palpate those that don't appear ready for breeding. He checks all visiting mares for sutures. It might be necessary to put in a breeding stitch, which is a cross-stitch that prevents tearing of the Caslick's sutures during breeding. The goal is to breed all mares immediately before ovulation. This may require the veterinarian to check and palpate mares around the clock, especially if a stallion's sperm are not long-lived.

The veterinarian monitors the stallion's health and potency. Samples of the stallion's sperm are collected after each cover and checked under the microscope for quality and quantity. If the stallion's fertility drops, you must depend on your veterinarian to discover it and deal with it.

The Need for a Good Teaser: A good teasing horse is a valuable and vital part of the staff on a breeding complex. While all mares were teased at their farm before arrival, those findings must be confirmed. It is the teaser's job to show you exactly what a mare will do when she is approached and mounted by the stallion. The teaser "courts" all visiting mares to determine if they are receptive to being bred. A good teaser may be any kind of a horse, from a pony stallion to a quiet Thoroughbred or Standardbred stallion. I like a full-sized horse for jumping maidens because his size approximates that of the stallion. The breed is not important - temperament and personality are everything. The good teaser is not rank or noisy. He is a wise fellow that approaches the mare cautiously, gauging her reaction at each step. He should not bite the mare and he must be manageable enough to be pulled off the mare after mounting her.

Often the first indication that a mare is in foal comes from the teaser. If he backs off mares that are beginning to show heat, chances are that these mares are 13 or 14 days in foal. The teaser knows this - he knows that these mares will kick him so he stays away.

The Importance of a Good Teasing Man: The teasing man supervises the use of the teaser, keeps the teasing charts and assists in the breeding shed. A superior teasing man is the most important person on your breeding team. An experienced teasing man is a keen observer of mares, understands their actions and can often predict whether a mare will be ready for breeding before the veterinarian examines her. A good teasing man has a computer-like memory. If he has seen the mare before, he will remember her and her reproductive behavior. It is not unusual for a competent teasing man

266

to recall that a particular mare comes into heat for five days and that she shows well and may be palpated with reliable results on the second day.

Unfortunately, the good teasing man is vanishing breed. The insight of an experienced teasing man observing the teasing process is disappearing from our body of knowledge. More and more breeders are relying completely on a teaser and on the veterinarian's opinion on a mare's reproductive status. The irony is, a veterinarian appreciates the skill of a good teasing man as much as anyone. If you have the chance to employ a good teasing man, do so. The combination of a qualified veterinarian, a good teaser and an experienced teasing man is unbeatable.

Is She Ready? A Process of Elimination: Your goal is to breed every mare just before she ovulates, impregnating her with one cover. Achieving this goal would be simple if every mare brought to your stallion were receptive to being bred and a few hours away (or minutes away) from ovulation. But this is not always the case. Mare management is not an exact science. Tight scheduling, human error and biological factors add variables to the situation. Every mare brought to your farm forces you to answer the question, "Is she ready?" Determining the correct answer consists of: 1) getting her history; and, 2) observing her actions in a controlled situation that simulates breeding.

Where did this mare come from and what do her records and teasing charts say? If you can't determine how this mare has been managed, she was probably mis-managed and the less background information there is, the riskier she becomes. Other risky mares are maiden mares, mares with a history of bad behavior and mares that have been mistreated. By contrast, well-managed mares have been under the lights and on a feeding program to manipulate their cycles. They were teased and checked regularly, the teasing charts are accurate and, as a result, they are usually easy to breed. Usually. My method is designed to make certain that *all* mares are ready for breeding.

1) All Mares Get Teased: The mare that is ready for breeding displays signs of heat. Her cycle was charted at the her farm and her actions are consistent with those of a mare in strong heat. To be absolutely certain that these findings are correct, she is teased again at the stallion complex. Teasing begins as soon as the mare is led off the van and into a holding stall. A holding stall is used for teasing to keep the mare's handler from being kicked or struck. The teaser approaches the mare in the same manner as the stallion, "talking," prancing and ready to breed. As he is led around the holding stall, the mare's reactions to these romantic overtures are carefully noted. Acceptance is shown by "breaking down," which means the mare stands with her hind legs apart, lifts her tail and urinates or "empties out." If the mare accepts the teaser and breaks down, she is considered ready to breed. This mare is not mounted by the teaser. She goes on to be washed, her cross-stitch is checked, her tail is bandaged and she is taken to the breeding shed and bred by the stallion.

2) Difficult Mares Are Teased and Jumped: The mare that stiffens, squeals or kicks while being teased or gives you any reason to suspect she is not ready for the stallion (including a history of being difficult to breed), requires additional measures. She is taken to the wash stall and a quick visual exam is done as she is washed. If she appears normal and healthy with good color to her vaginal tissues, she is taken to the breeding shed. Here, she teased again. Next, she is twitched and the breeding shield and leg strap are put on, just as they will be when she is mounted by the stallion. The teaser must mount these unreceptive mares while wearing a shield that prevents penetration. Now the teaser mounts her, just as the stallion will later do. Most mares will break down at this point and go on to breed perfectly with the stallion.

3) Problem Mares Require Research: If the mare fights the teaser when she is jumped, if she kicks at him or tries to run over the staff, put her in a stall. A mare that has been teased repeatedly and jumped by the teaser but does not break down, requires research. Call the mare manager or veterinarian at her home farm. Ask when she was last teased and palpated and what were the results. Obtain permission to have your veterinarian examine the mare. Your veterinarian may find one of two things: (1) the mare is in heat and has yet to ovulate, which means she must be teased and jumped periodically until she breaks down; or, (2) she has already ovulated, in which case she must be sent home. Never attempt to breed a mare that has already ovulated and refuses the teaser. She will fight the teaser, she will fight the stallion and she will not get in foal.

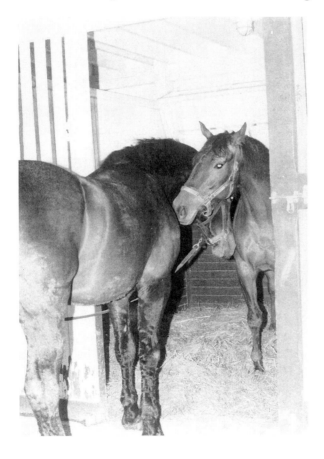

The Teasing Process: Photo 1 shows a mare receptive to the teaser. This is a good indication that she is ready to be bred.
(Photo courtesy of Suzie Oldham)

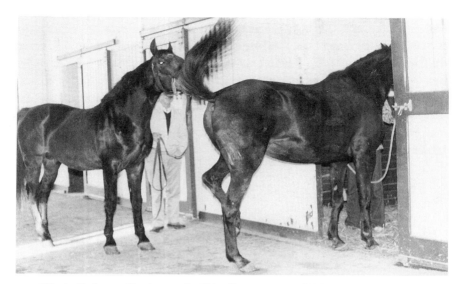

Photo 2 shows the teaser "talking" to a mare which is not ready for breeding. Her body language clearly says, "Go away!"

(Photo courtesy of Suzie Oldham)

4) Maiden Mares Need Training: With maiden mares, it is necessary to determine that they are psychologically ready for breeding. The maiden must be introduced to the restraints you will use in the breeding shed and she must be jumped by the teaser before she is put to the stallion.

First, introduce her to the equipment. She must learn to tolerate the twitch on her nose, the breeding pad or shield on her neck (a leather or canvas cover which protects her withers in case the stallion bites her) and the leg strap. The leg strap holds a foreleg up, forcing the mare to keep both hind feet on the ground. If hobbles are to be used, she must be trained to accept them.

Unless you are certain that the maiden was jumped before, have your teaser jump her. Take the mare to the breeding shed and put the shield on her neck. Allow the teaser to approach the mare and talk to her. When she is calm, put the twitch on her nose and leg strap her (if you plan to breed with hobbles use them now). The teaser is wearing the teasing shield that prevents him from entering and breeding the mare. Allow the teaser to jump the maiden, releasing her leg strap once he is securely up. Now you know what to expect and so does she. Do not put the maiden mare to the stallion until she has these experiences.

The Cover: The act of breeding is a risky business. Things happen fast in the breeding shed. There's always the chance of someone, human or horse, being injured. The key to avoiding accidents is careful planning and preparation. Accidents usually result when someone is in a hurry and skips a step or two. I've never seen an accident that couldn't have been prevented by careful preparation.

The ideal number of helpers in the breeding shed is five. While most covers proceed uneventfully and don't require five people, there is always the possibility for problems. When something goes wrong, the fourth or fifth person can make the difference between an incident and an accident. Consider the value of the animals involved and how much an accident can cost you. It's foolish to go into the breeding shed understaffed.

The Eight Steps of the Cover: There are faster methods than mine, but the breeding shed is a place where hastiness is penalized. Achieving high conception rates with no accidents requires the following eight steps.

Step one: The mare is teased and shown be to ready for breeding. Her records are double-checked - her identity and the stallion to which she is to be bred are verified.

Step two: The mare's genitals are washed thoroughly with a solution of non-spermicidal cleanser recommended by your veterinarian. Her cross-stitch is checked and replaced if necessary. Her tail is bandaged to keep loose hairs out of the way.

Step three: The mare is taken into the breeding shed. One person is positioned at her head, holding the halter and ready to apply the twitch. A second person is at her shoulder. He puts the shield on her neck. It is also his job to put on and release the leg strap and to

271

steady the mare. A third person stands at her hindquarters, ready to pull her tail out of the way and to steady her if necessary.

Step four: The stallion is taken to the wash rack. His penis is rinsed with water only. (Clear water is used so as not to damage the sperm. The stallion was washed with soap following the previous cover.)

Step five: The stallion handler leads the stallion toward the mare's side. The stallion needs to sniff the mare's flanks and "talk" to the mare to become fully excited and ready for breeding. When he becomes ready, he is backed up a few steps while the mare is restrained. The twitch is put on her nose and a front leg is strapped up. This is a critical moment when the stallion handler needs all his skill and experience. The stallion may have entered the breeding shed in an excited state. He needs a certain amount of time to become ready to breed, but he may become difficult to handle if he's delayed too long while the mare is being restrained. This demands good timing from the stallion handler. As he begins backing the stallion, he directs the mare's handlers to restrain her. By the time the stallion is backed to a position behind the mare, the restraints are in place. The stallion is positioned directly behind the mare so he can mount her easily and safely. The stallion must not mount the mare from the side, which could cause problems or injuries. As the stallion goes up to mount the mare, the third man pulls her tail out of the way.

Step six: As the horse mounts the mare, the stallion handler guides the penis into the mare. The fifth person follows behind, carrying a styrofoam cup to catch any fluid that drips off the stallion's penis after the cover. This person with the cup may also assist with guiding the stallion into the mare. The person at the mare's hindquarters holds her tail out of the way and may brace her hindquarters to steady her and keep her from swaying sideways. The moment the stallion is securely on top of the mare, her leg strap is released. The leg strap person may steady the mare or hold the stallion's foreleg to steady him, whichever is needed. The person holding the mare's halter and the twitch holds the mare still, keeping her from moving forward more than a step and preventing her from backing up, which is more serious. If the mare backs up into the stallion, she could cause him to lose his balance and fall backwards.

Photo of the start of the cover, showing everyone at their places and the stallion approaching to mount the mare.

(Photo courtesy of Z)

Step seven: After the stallion has ejaculated, which is usually shown by "flagging" or short rises of the tail in quick succession, the stallion is taken off the mare. At the same moment, the mare handler leads the mare forward and then quickly to the side, moving her hindquarters away from the stallion as quickly as possible. As the stallion dismounts, the cup is used to catch any fluid that drips from the horse's penis. The fluid is put under the microscope to look for semen, which verifies ejaculation. If ejaculation did not occur, the cover is repeated in a few minutes. However, if ejaculation occurred as the stallion was coming off the mare, a large amount of the ejaculate could be in the cup, perhaps as much as 30 to 40 cc. In this case, the mare is impregnated with it artificially.

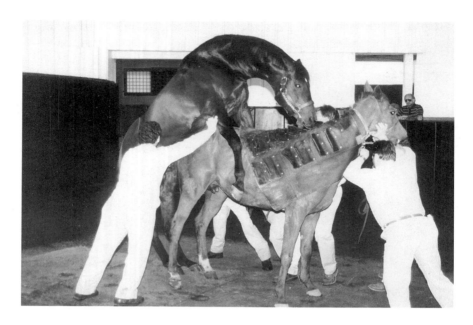

Photo of a successful cover. Note the positions of the handlers as they steady both mare and stallion.

(Photo courtesy of Martin Pierce)

Step eight: The stallion is taken to the wash rack and his penis is washed with a antiseptic soap, then he is returned to his paddock or stall. The mare is not washed. She may be walked around to prevent her from urinating and straining.

Avoiding Misunderstandings: The best farms videotape the cover, a procedure which I recommend. I've seen mix-ups and accusations which could have been avoided with a videotape. If a mare owner says his mare wasn't covered or you didn't use the right horse, you have proof. Show him the videotape.

Sperm Lifespan and Double Breedings: Good .i. management means avoiding needless covers. Knowing the life span of a 's sperm is one of the keys to managing him. While the average life span is 48 hours, some stallion's sperm live for as long as 90 hours. Other stallions have "fragile" sperm that only live for 10 or 12 hours. Knowing this is important for saving covers.

Establishing a life span is a two-part process. The drippings collected from every cover are put on a slide and checked under the microscope. The checks reveal a pattern of how long the sperm live in the lab.

The second and truest test of sperm life is how long they remain viable inside the mare. This is determined by charting the time between a pregnant mare's cover and subsequent ovulation. If a mare was covered on Wednesday noon and she ovulated on Friday at noon, the resulting pregnancy tells you that the stallion's sperm are viable for at least 48 hours. Keep records of every breeding and subsequent ovulation. These figures may appear to change from time to time, but over the season a true picture of sperm lifespan will emerge. Keeping these statistics accurately is the best method for getting this information.

If the mare ovulates 10 hours after the first cover and you know your stallion's sperm live for 48 hours, you won't waste your stallion and risk the first good cover with a double breeding. If your stallion has particularly long-lived sperm, say 80 hours, you may need to do very few doubles throughout the season. Such a stallion can often accommodate a larger number of mares per season than the average horse.

Frequency of Covers: How many times can you breed a per day? It depends on the horse. A well-managed stallion is able to make about 130 to 140 covers over the course of the season and a few stallions can make as many as 160 covers. The bulk of these covers, perhaps 120 out of the total, will take place early in the season, during February, March and April. This means the stallion breeds 40 or more times a month for the first three months.

Structure each week's breeding schedule to allow one day off and another day to catch up on unexpected problems, such as mares that come in for breeding sooner or later than expected. Don't plan a six-day breeding schedule. The season is hectic enough that five days of breeding often turn into six and you must not eliminate the stallion's weekly day off. Plan your five-day period for using the horse, planning two to three breedings a day which may be scheduled in the morning, the afternoon or in the evening.

Ultimately, the horse determines how many covers will be accomplished. Monitor the stallion's enthusiasm and the lab analysis of the drippings to tell if he is losing his interest or potency. If you see the volume of ejaculate drop (70 cc is the average and 100 cc is common for healthy stallions) or notice that the stallion appears dull, you may need to cut back. Maybe five times a week is enough for a particular stallion. But most stallions can make 12 to 15 covers a week without a problem. If you're feeding and exercising him correctly, he can do this easily all season long. While at Gainesway, I was the first manager to keep the breeding shed open during the evening, which allowed us to use stallions three times a day. This became Gainesway's policy and now many farms use their stallions three times a day.

Chapter 13

Feeding Horses

Good nutrition can make the difference between breeding and raising a top horse or a mediocre one. This is one area where you can get a jump on your competition. I believe that the horse which gets proper nutrition, starting before he's even born and continuing every day of his life, is the horse that will be as good as his genes and his training can make him. He'll race to his potential. He won't break down as easily as other horses. He'll lead a long, productive life.

When I got into the horse business over 40 years ago, oats and good timothy hay were considered the best feeds for horses. Thought to provide the right amounts of protein, vitamins, minerals and bulk, they were safe feeds, tolerated by nearly all horses.

Then trainers and breeders started to borrow ideas from other areas of agriculture. Noting the tremendous size and weight gains made by cattle fed on alfalfa and soybean-based grain mixtures, they started feeding horses like feeder cattle. High protein and high energy rations were in every feed room. The horses grew faster, too. Foals grew faster, and yearlings were much taller than those of years past. Auction buyers were delighted with the big, muscular yearlings at the sales. Two-year-olds were the size of three-year-olds. Everyone was obsessed with the goal of producing the biggest horses in the shortest amount of time by using the new nutritional programs.

Something happened along the way. These bigger, faster-growing horses didn't run any faster. But they did break down faster. For reasons not completely understood, their bones and joints did not develop normal strength. At racing speeds, they broke down, sometimes with tragic consequences.

While I cannot say with certainty that alfalfa hay causes horses to break down, there have been studies that implicate over-feeding of certain nutrients with developmental disorders. For me and for many breeders of racehorses, equine nutrition has come full circle. We have returned to the simple, time-honored methods of feeding horses. Good pastures, green timothy hay and quality oats are far superior to alfalfa and other high energy diets. Fit but not fat are the watchwords for maintaining normal development.

The difference between feeding horses today and back in the old days, is that then we fed what we *believed* to be good rations. Today we feed what science has measured and quantified to be the right nutrients, in the right amounts.

There are specific, ascertainable nutritional requirements of the horse that vary according to the stage of life. The best way to provide the nutritional requirements is through a careful balance of the traditional feeds of grass, hay and grain. The task, then, is to determine what the horse needs at every stage for optimum development with a minimum of risk, and how to best supply these needs in a form that is natural, available and readily assimilated by the horse.

Established Nutritional Guidelines: Scientists have established the basic nutritional requirements for all horses, of all ages and involved in all types of work. Established guidelines are available from the National Research Council. Their most recent report (1989 as of this writing) details the horse's requirements for energy, crude protein, fat, vitamins, macro-minerals (including the critical calcium/phosphorus ratios), micro-minerals and fiber. These nutritional needs are broken down into specific categories, such as growing horses (lactating mares, weanlings, yearlings, etc.), and nutritional requirements according to weight and use (idle horses, moderate work, intense work, breeding stallions, etc.).

From the NRC report we learn, for instance, that pregnant mares require 10% crude protein in the diet until the 11th month, when the crude protein must be increased to 10.6%. The protein requirements of this pregnant mare are further expressed in grams as

278

well as percentages. Vitamins, macro-minerals and all other components of the horse's diet are analyzed in similar detail.

After the nutritional needs of every type of horse are described, the NRC gives nutritional analyses of all types of hay, grasses and grains, each expressed in tables showing its contribution to the optimum equine diet. Each type of grass, hay and grain is further analyzed according to stage of growth, such as early fresh stage, vegetative stage, early bloom, mid-bloom. Kentucky bluegrass, for example, jumps in protein from 5.4% in its early stage to 17.4% in the vegetative stage, while maintaining a relatively stable calcium/phosphorus ratio (0.15%/0.14% to 0.50% /0.44%). The NRC has analyzed everything and anything you could possibly feed a horse, including anchovy (fish) meal. It should be a simple matter to look up your grass and hay, find a grain that complements it and match it to the horses you're feeding.

Well, it isn't simple. It would be nice if you could feed the same hay the NRC used for their tests, but you can't. The grass they tested wasn't grown on your land, either. Your horses will graze in your pastures and eat your hay and I guarantee you they will not provide exactly the same nutrients in the same proportions listed in the NRC table. And, can you be certain you are interpreting the tables correctly - *exactly* when does your grass go from the early, fresh stage to the vegetative stage? The change in nutritional value can be dramatic and you must recognize when it occurs so you can provide the correct grain mixture to complement it.

And while the NRC guidelines are extensive as far as each stage of the horse's growth, they don't tell you exactly when your horse passes from one stage into the next. When does a yearling's requirements change from those of moderate growth to rapid growth, or from those of a normal yearling to a long yearling? When is a two-year-old doing light work and when does it become moderate work? And what about the different growth patterns and specialized needs of individual horses? You cannot feed two 14-month-old horses exactly the same and do right by both of them. NRC standards are broad guidelines. Benefiting from them requires expert interpretation and constant monitoring and adjustments. You may follow these guidelines to the letter but, without expert help, you will always be at variance with them.

Feeding a horse is a matter of supplying protein, carbohydrates, fat, vitamins, minerals and roughage. While these requirements can be met in many ways, the art and science of feeding is to provide these basic nutrients in the proper amounts and exact proportions. Enough roughage must be supplied to keep the intestinal tract working smoothly. Too much fiber in the diet shorts the animal of other needed nutrients. Fat is a necessary requirement, but oversupplying fat can stress the skeletal frame. Enough protein must be available to realize the animal's genetic potential for growth. Too much protein or an imbalance of minerals can cause developmental disorders, such as epiphysitis or osteochondritis dessicans (OCD). Such disorders of the bones, joints and cartilage can cripple an otherwise healthy horse and devastate a breeding program. The key is to supply the necessary nutrients in the correct proportions without oversupplying any one or shorting another.

Nutritional requirements are not static, but change at each stage of life. The broodmare needs to provide a strong skeleton to the developing fetus without robbing her own system of nutrients. Her nutritional requirements change while she is nursing her foal and change again when the foal is weaned. The growing suckling, weanling and yearling must be fed different, precise mixtures to achieve size and strength without risking developmental disorders. The racehorse in training needs proper nutrition to remain sound and competitive to answer the challenge of the racetrack. Finally, the horse at stud has specific needs for maintaining energy and fertility without compromising soundness. Every horse has different requirements at different stages of life that must be met to achieve and maintain genetic potential.

The Nutritional Consultant: I would like to give you Joe Taylor's secret formula for feeding horses, but I don't have one. What I feed my horses this month may be entirely different than what I feed next month. What I feed on Farm A may be completely different than what I feed on Farm B.

The key to a scientific feeding program is to test your grass and hay for nutritional value and then supplement whatever is lacking by feeding the correct grain mixture. But to do this, a standard for proper nutrition, an ideal equine diet must first be established. Next, a way must be found to provide and monitor it. This is why every farm needs the services of a qualified equine nutritionist as much as it needs the services of a qualified veterinarian.

Our choice at *Taylor Made Farms* is a nutritional consultant who maintains an extensive database of information on the nutritional requirements of the equine athlete. His philosophy is that optimum nutrition is not a radical shift from established guidelines, but the critically engineered balance of nutrients for the appropriate stage of development, fed in correct amounts and monitored conscientiously.

The program we developed for *Taylor Made Farms* has four facets: (1) We regularly test the nutritional value of our grass and hay. (2) For each type of horse, a ration is formulated which complements our grass, since grass forms the basis of our horses' diets. This ration is engineered and balanced according to more than 60 different nutrients, all recognized as necessary components of equine nutrition. (3) Each horse is fed according to his stage of life and his own particular needs. For example, all yearlings do not receive the same amount; each is fed as an individual. (4) Careful monitoring assures that each horse is growing and developing according to its own potential. Feed is administered by qualified personnel who are trained to look closely at the horse and note changes day to day. Horses are checked regularly by management who have the superior eye to recognize optimum growth and spot potential problems. Monthly checks of all foals and yearlings by the nutritional consultant coincide with monthly measurements of weight, height, heartgirth, gaskin and cannon bone circumference. These measurements are entered into the computer and compared against the records maintained by the nutritional consultant. A profile is developed for each horse which can be correlated to the extensive data already on hand.

Our nutritional program, while time-consuming and not inexpensive, is the most advanced and comprehensive available. The result is a superior horse. If producing a superior horse is your most important goal, I recommend that you adopt a scientific nutritional program. While you may choose to feed your horses according to your eye, which is the traditional method, be aware of the shortcomings. You cannot see beneath the skin to the bones, muscles and ligaments. You cannot see minute changes in size and weight. Take advantage of the options offered by technology.

How to Find a Nutritionist: Choosing your nutritionist will involve some research. Talk with a number of veterinarians or call your closest university or veterinary school. Get the names of nutritionists from other breeders who produce sound, healthy horses. Interview prospective nutritionists. Spend time discussing your goals and make sure the expert you select understands them. This is one area where "well begun is half done."

Your nutritional expert will begin by reviewing the most up-to-date nutritional requirements with you. It is necessary to first define the optimum nutritional needs of the horse. With a standard defined, he can determine the most effective program to meet this ideal. The task is to coordinate your grass, hay and grain, and any necessary supplementation to meet the established ideal.

Good Nutrition Begins with Good Grass and Hay: In a perfect world, all we would need is grass. The horse evolved as a grazing animal, consuming large quantities of low-quality forage. Good grass contains all required nutrients in a form that is easily assimilated by the horse. Unfortunately, grass is usually not as good as we would like it to be. Compounding the problem is that for much of the year, horses must be fed hay instead of grass. Our job is to: (1) produce the best quality of grass possible; and, (2) when grass is not available, feed the best quality hay possible; and, (3) add to the horse's diet whatever is lacking in the grass or hay.

The place to begin this program is in your pastures. The most natural, complete and economical food for horses is quality grass, so begin with the aim of producing the best grass your land can grow. Annual soil tests are necessary to determine the fertilizers needed to maintain good grass. Proper fertilization assures uniformity of grass quality from pasture to pasture.

Test the grass itself for nutritional value by having the clippings analyzed. Be sure to test each pasture and paddock, as soil and grass can change from one section of land to the next. After you have established what your grass does and does not provide, work backwards to fill the deficiencies with the grain.

Test your grass a minimum of four times a year. The nutritional value of pasture grass changes from season to season. In spring, the grass is rich and lush, high in protein but lacking fiber. Summer grasses are different, stemmier but richer in other nutrients. As the seasons change, so must the grain ration. Reformulate your feed as the quality of your pasture changes.

Quality Hay: Hay is the next step. Test your hay for quality, then calculate how much of the ration is provided by hay at different times of the year. This will vary, as horses depend on hay for much of the ration in the winter, while in summer they may only need a few daily pounds for roughage.

I recommend timothy hay. Good timothy is green, leafy and palatable to horses. It provides roughage and strength to horses without being too high in protein or any one mineral. I believe that alfalfa hay is less valuable in a feeding program. Timothy is safer to feed free choice than is alfalfa hay.

When buying timothy hay, check for the green color and slightly flexible texture that tells you the hay hasn't been dried too much. The head of the timothy should be short, an inch or less, with the seeds clinging tightly. There should be leaves on the stalks. If the hay is so dry that it shatters and the seeds and leaves fall off, it's too dry.

Buy all your hay from the same supplier if possible. Find out what region of the country the hay comes from, and specify that you want hay grown on the same land. If your barn is filled with hay from several different regions of the country, you will have hay with varying nutritional values and no single grain mixture will supplement them correctly. When you have a reliable source for hay, you ensure a stable source of nutrients.

Grain Completes the Equation: When nutritional values are established for your grass and hay, determine what must be added to provide a balanced diet. Traditionally, horsemen have fed oats to complement their hay and grass. Oats are an excellent horse feed. They are easily digested and widely available. But all oats are not created equal. To achieve the maximum benefit from your feeding program, it is necessary to periodically test the oats, corn, barley and whatever else may go into the mixture. It may be necessary to find another source of oats to maintain a high quality. Regular testing assures you of a stable supply of nutrients.

With values established, formulate a precise mixture of grains, vitamins and minerals. This mixture, combined with your grass and hay, should satisfy the requirements set by the NRC as modified by your nutrition expert to fit your particular circumstances.

The grain mixture must be adjusted for growing and mature horses, and further refined for performance horses and less active stock. Sucklings, weanlings, yearlings, mares in the various stages of pregnancy, nursing mares, stallions, racehorses, and retired horses all have different nutritional needs. The end result must be several different ready-to-feed mixtures for all types of horses.

The grain mixture must be adjusted seasonally to complement the changes in the pasture grass. In winter, the grain must be reformulated again to complement the hay that now forms the bulk of the horse's diet.

Avoid Supplements and Commercial Feeds: Eliminate the common practice of adding supplements at feeding time. Everything the horse needs for good nutrition should be supplied by the combination of your grass, hay and grain. Supplements are too difficult to feed correctly, consequently they waste money. Don't rely on them.

Pre-packaged feeds are based on the nutritional assumptions of the manufacturer. They are not based on the specific nutritional needs of your horses. The manufacturer does not have the advantage of knowing the nutritional value of your grass and hay. However well-formulated, they cannot provide optimum nutrition to your horses.

Avoid Copying Feeding Programs: The soil in every part of the country varies. Each farm is different and nutritional values may even change from one field to another. The nutritional program implemented on the neighbor's farm is probably wrong for you. The only way for you to devise a feed that will yield optimum results is to test your grass and hay and formulate a customized grain mixture. Adopting someone else's exact feed or any commercial feed will not only fail to meet the standard, it could even be detrimental to the health of your horses.

Monitor the Results: Weigh every horse monthly. "Eyeballing" is not accurate enough to produce best results. A scale will tell you if the horse is gaining, losing or maintaining.

Each month measure the height, bone and heart-girth of all young horses. This will alert you and your nutritionist to growth spurts that must be carefully monitored. It is possible for a young horse to grow too fast. You may need to adjust a yearling's feed to avoid problems. Stay on top of the growth of your young horses - it's the best way to avoid growth disorders and breakdowns.

Once a day, walk through your barn. Look at the horses. Note how they clean up their feed and check the appearance of the manure for dryness, which can signal constipation or large amounts of whole oats, which may mean a tooth problem. Check their expressions, the look in their eyes, the attitude of their ears, the shine of their coats and the quality of their hooves. The finest feeding program is doomed to fail if not administered and monitored by a good horseman, so take note of the smallest details. Meticulous care combined with observation is the best recipe for success.

How to Feed Horses: Feeding horses in the proper way is as important as using the right feeds. The best grain is wasted if the horse is bullied by the others and can't eat it. A good management tool is to bring all horses inside to be fed at least once a day. This allows each horse to eat without having to compete for the food he needs.

Bringing horses inside once a day for feeding gives you a chance to look them over carefully for injuries, illness or other problems. If the horse is injured, you must be able to treat the injury without chasing the animal around the pasture. A good horseman uses feeding time to teach the animal to trust people, to encourage being caught and to consider it a reward by being led inside to a meal. While the horse is meant to live outside, coming inside once a day for a meal is important to the horse's health and education.

Feed good timothy hay free choice to all horses, all year, even when they are living out on pasture. Horses need a lot of roughage in their diet. Many of the colics that coincide with lush, green pasture can be avoided by keeping hay in front of the horse at all times. Never allow a horse to go out to pasture hungry. Always provide clean timothy hay for roughage and to take the edge off the appetite.

Mineral Blocks: All horses need access to a good mineral block in the pasture or paddock. I like Morton mineral blocks because they have a good balance of minerals and salt, and horses will eat them. If these blocks are supplied to each horse, you will eliminate most tail-chewing, fence chewing, bark-stripping and root-gnawing. The horse needs minerals. Supply them in a safe, palatable form and you will eliminate many common vices.

Provide one mineral block to each paddock and one block per three horses in a pasture. Do not put out a plain salt block, because the horses will eat the salt block but not get the minerals they need. Additional salt can be provided in the grain mixture, but it should not be supplied as a plain salt block.

Don't put all your mineral blocks in one area. Place them in several spots so each horse has access to a block without being bullied by another. Mineral blocks may be placed in a line and be moved regularly.

Feeding Yearlings: Our yearlings are fed inside twice a day and outside once a day. They come in every morning at 7:00 a.m. We're always on time, so they're waiting for us at the gate. They eat a ration of grain at 7:00 a.m. and again at 11:00 a.m. These grain rations are fed in varying amounts, according to how much a particular yearling needs to maintain condition and growth. At 1:00 p.m., all the yearlings are turned outside again. At 4:00 p.m. we give them each about five pounds of grain outside.

It's a good practice to have only one person feeding a horse. This is accomplished by using feed bags. These are canvas bags that hang on the front of the stall. The morning groom mixes all the day's feed for that horse. He feeds the horse inside its stall at 11:00 a.m., outside at 4:00 p.m. and puts the next morning's ration into the feed bag. The ration is ready for the night man to put into the feed tub at 5:00 a.m. When the horse is brought inside at 7:00 a.m. the feed is waiting for him. This way, the horse is never shorted or overfed by mistake. Most tack or horse equipment shops sell these feed bags. You can buy them in your stable colors or have them custom-made at a tent and awning shop.

Grain is fed in tubs in the stall. The tubs must be checked after each meal. Uneaten grain means the horse is getting too much and the ration must be cut down. Uneaten grain must always be discarded. If grain is left in the tub, it will turn sour and eventually mold, which will make the horse sick.

Supply hay free-choice, all year round. Hay should always be available, in the pastures and in the stalls. The yearlings will eat hay from hay racks in the field. Set hay racks and troughs in a well-drained area, away from fences. One 10-foot hay rack will serve eight colts, four on each side. If you have 16 horses, put the second rack about 30 feet away from the first.

Outside, yearlings may eat their grain from piles on the ground. Here's my method for ground-feeding: Place all the mineral blocks in a row, about sixty feet apart. Starting at the first mineral block, put down a small flake of hay and pour the grain ration on top of the hay. Walk 25 to 30 feet toward the next mineral block and put down another hay/grain pile. Put a third pile 30 feet from the second, staying on the line between the mineral blocks. By using the mineral blocks as reference points, you will see exactly where the horses were fed last. Any uneaten feed will be apparent and can be removed before it goes sour. Move or roll the blocks a few feet each day, choosing a clean spot for each feeding. Never put hay or grain in an area that is trampled or bare of grass. Every few days, straighten the mineral blocks to maintain the line. The straight line is important. Don't feed horses in a circle. They will eat more quietly if the piles are in a straight line.

Feeding Broodmares: Broodmares are separated into three groups, according to reproductive status. Each group is fed according to its needs. After November, all mares come onto the same schedule of eating their morning feed in the barn.

Broodmares with foals are fed grain once in the morning in their stalls and again in the evening outside. Grain is placed on flakes of hay for the evening meal outside, in the manner described for yearlings. Check the ground after the mares have eaten their grain. The mare that leaves grain uneaten is either sick or she needs her ration cut down.

Mares whose foals have been weaned are fed grain once a day outside. Barren and maiden mares are fed the same way. These mares do not come into the barn until November.

Free-choice hay should be supplied to all mares. Broodmare pastures need one or two hayracks which are always stocked with hay. You will see one mare or another eating from the rack almost all the time. Put some hay on the ground for broodmares, too. A group of broodmares usually will not eat quietly from a hayrack. One bossy broodmare will take up the whole side of the hayrack, kicking at any other mares that approach. Only when she is finished can another, more timid mare eat from the rack. No broodmare should have to fight for the hay she needs - supply hay both in the racks and on the ground.

Stallions: Stallions need free-choice timothy hay and a 12% protein grain ration fed to weight and condition. The requirements of weight and condition may vary greatly from the breeding season to the rest of the year. Weigh all stallions monthly to keep them at their ideal weight.

Some stallions need a substantial increase in feed when they are covering mares. It is vital to supply them with the nutrients and energy they need to produce healthy sperm and settle their mares. Other stallions put on weight too easily. If not carefully monitored and exercised, they will enter the breeding season soft and fat. Extra weight stresses the legs of the and can even cause him to lose interest in his mares. Allowing a stallion to become overly fat is poor management, commonly done but easily avoided.

These broodmares eat their grain outside. The grain is placed on their hay and the piles are in a straight line.

(Photo courtesy of Martin Pierce)

Chapter 14

Managing Employees

Every business seeks to hire the most competent and ambitious employees it can find and afford. That is, every business except the horse business. The horse industry is the only place you will still find expensive capital investments (horses) put in the hands of employees whose only motivation for working is the promise of a warm place to sleep and enough money to buy a bottle of liquor. Many farm owners and managers still think they cannot afford or attract motivated employees. They are wrong.

Equal Opportunity: I want to clarify an important point. When I started in the horse business as a young man, nearly all professionals were men. The teasing man was a *man*, as was the foaling *man*, and you might read about a famous horse*man*. Times have changed - women occupy many of these positions today and many of the industry's top veterinarians, managers and trainers are women. Each person brings certain strengths to a job and gender is not important. At *Taylor Made*, we hire on the basis of talent and enthusiasm, not sex. This gives us a real advantage by having a much larger labor pool from which to draw and you should do the same. Nonetheless, the term "man" remains as part of my vocabulary, so when I say foaling man or mare man or make some other reference to the male gender, I'm referring to both men and women equally.

The Importance of Grooms: The most important employee on any farm is the groom. The groom is intimately involved with the horse. He feeds the horse and protects it from harm, ministers to its needs and spots small problems before they become major. The attitude and diligence with which the groom attends his horse plays a key role in its ultimate success or failure. Your farm will continue to operate for a time without you and it will even run for a while without your farm manager or foremen. But it won't run very long without the grooms.

Unfortunately, the economics of the horse business are such that grooms must be paid relatively low wages. What a farm can afford to pay a groom is far less than what a good groom is really worth. Finding and keeping people who will work the long hours, do the menial chores and who will perform their tasks with pride and dedication is a tall order. The key to hiring good grooms is: 1) Attract and hire the right people in the first place; and 2) keep the good people doing good work by training them, encouraging them and offering them the chance for advancement.

Attracting the Right Grooms: Grooms feed and water the horses, clean the horses, clean the stalls, clean the aisles and the storage rooms and the tack and the windows. They wrestle bales, remove cobwebs, pick dead birds out of waterers and manure out of drains. It is hard, dirty and repetitive work and it must be done in all kinds of weather. It is not for everyone and somewhere between the smashed toes and the frozen fingers, your average unskilled, unmotivated employee is going to let some important details slide.

The only kind of person who will do this kind of work responsibly and enthusiastically is someone who believes his hard work is going to get him somewhere. It is important that the groom be a person who aspires to rise in the horse business and who sees the role of groom as a ground-floor opportunity to learn the business and to move up in it. Seek out these people, train them and inspire them. You must groom the groom to be a farm manager, a trainer or something more than a groom.

Hiring good grooms takes skill and intuition. Most applicants will be entry-level people with questionable skills and aptitude for the work. I look for certain backgrounds and personality traits. Someone who worked at a job that required hard work and involved animals is a good candidate. Maybe he's been working for a kennel or on a dairy farm, which tells you he understands hard work. If this person wants to learn, I can offer him a chance to acquire new skills and improve his station in life. If a groom has the ambition to become a mare man or another type of specialist, we work with him to achieve that goal.

People seem to fall into two categories: those who are neat and organized by nature and those who are not. Good grooms are in the first category. A man once told me that if you want to hire grooms who will keep your place neat and clean, have breakfast with the prospective employee! Go to his house and eat breakfast with him and see how he lives, he told me. While this may not always be possible, I think it's true and you should keep it in mind when you interview people.

Young People: Consider hiring young people. There are many young men and women who want a career in the horse industry. Help them to gain the knowledge to fulfill their dreams and you have access to a labor pool that is both dedicated and affordable. At *Taylor Made*, we are so enthused about hiring and training young people that we have an intern program. A young man or woman who wants a career in horses will receive instruction and a groom's wages in return for work. Our interns give us affordable, responsible and sober labor. We give them the knowledge and skills needed to succeed in this business. It's a fair exchange.

The education of interns is both theoretical and hands-on. The goal is to develop their skills and move them up in the scope of their responsibilities. Our Intern program has been a success - the young people we've hired have learned and grown with us. Many have gone on to take their places at the top levels of the industry.

Getting Grooms Started: I start most employees at the bottom, painting fences or running the weedeater. The entry-level employee on a breeding farm must learn to "catch the pony before he can ride him." This means that all employees will learn the basics about handling and caring for horses before they are put in charge of a horse. They need to know the correct way to clean a stall and how to drive the tractor and spreader down the aisle without tearing the doors off. They should clean the barn and blow the aisles and get it done quickly. They should know how to brush a horse, clean out its feet and take its temperature. They should learn to monitor the horses' legs and report any swelling, heat or other problems.

Our grooms learn first by observation, then by instruction. I don't assume that a groom can lead a horse in and out safely. I have him show me how he does it. When a groom or an intern shows me he is competent at his level of responsibilities, I instruct him in more advanced duties.

Learning new skills encourages grooms and brings out special talents and aptitudes. A more advanced groom is able to exercise yearlings in the round pen or on the treadmill. Another person might be good with foals and enjoy halter-breaking them or attending to their medical needs. You may have a groom who is good with the rasp and wants to watch and learn from the farrier. Encourage your grooms to acquire the special skills that make them more useful employees. They will realize that promotion comes from performance. This is a simple method, but it is hands-on and it has produced many professionals for the racing industry.

Keeping and Promoting Good Grooms: How well your employees perform will depend, in a large part, on how they're treated. I believe that most people are basically good and that they need to be taught and uplifted, not put down. Don't make the mistake of thinking that your minimum wage groom isn't worth much because you're not paying him a manager's salary and don't let your managers and foremen make this mistake, either. Your managers must: 1) Treat grooms with respect. 2) Listen to their comments about the horses in their charge. 3) Train and promote those grooms who acquire knowledge and want more responsibility.

Hang on to a good groom by giving him something more than a paycheck. Give him encouragement to sustain him through the long hours. Give him your respect which becomes the self-respect that gets him to work on time, every day. Most important, give him the knowledge and skills to move on to a better job. Promotion made on the basis of merit sends a clear message: Work hard and learn and you will move up in this organization. As your reputation for advancement grows, so will the number and the quality of people seeking to work for you. Fair promotion due to hard work and new skills is universally recognized - you will find it relatively easy to replace the promoted groom.

Turnover: No matter how well you run your farm, the attrition of good employees is inevitable. There are two ways to view this. One school of thought says that losing good people is an inconvenience without any redeeming aspects. Try to avoid it by paying much higher wages or chalk it up to the cost of doing business. I am of the second school, which suggests that losing good grooms to other employers may be good public relations. Well-trained grooms and other employees are ambassadors whose skill and discipline advertise your farm more effectively than any full-color advertisement possibly could. Employees who go on to bigger and better things will remember where they got their start and refer business back to you.

Take pride in how many people working for your competitors learned their job and got their start from you. Offer your references and use your connections to help place your "graduates." When your farm loses a good groom to a top trainer, your reputation will be enhanced by that groom's good work. If the broodmare manager you trained goes to work for a competitor, wish him well. His expertise will speak volumes about your farm. This may be a simple philosophy, but I have trained more farm managers than anybody in the business.

Farm Manager: The farm manager is at the top of the professional hierarchy. He has the most comprehensive knowledge of horses and the ultimate responsibility for them. Hire the very best you can find. If you compromise here, your other managers had better be outstanding.

Look for the person who has experience from a good, well-run farm. Ask for references and follow up on them. Someone who is willing to take classes, to read and study to improve himself and who is enthused about your operation is a good prospect.

The size of your farm will help determine the type of farm manager you need. The larger the farm, the more specialization required among farm employees. The manager of a large farm is an executive whose responsibilities often take him away from the day-to-day operations. The smaller the farm, the more versatility demanded of its manager. The small farm requires a hands-on manager who can fill anyone's shoes. On a farm of fewer than 50 mares, the farm manager may double as one of the two mare managers, as the stallion manager or as the yearling manager. He is probably the farm's salesman and director of advertising, too.

The farm manager must understand human nature as well as horses. He must make his people feel valuable. His employees will work hard and pay attention to details only if he can motivate them to do so. This is where many owners get into trouble. They hire a manager with a lot of horse experience, but who is short on people skills.

There are a few types of managers to avoid. Watch out for the guy who knows everything. A good manager speaks his mind, but he also knows when to say "I don't know." The guy who thinks he knows everything most assuredly does not. His kind of expertise is expensive in the long run.

Similar to the know-it-all, is the big talker. He may give a good impression, but he doesn't get much done. He won't give you a day's work for a day's pay and neither will the people under him. Anytime a manager comes to you and says that the help he's got is no good, you'd better get rid of him. He's the one who is no good. The people in his employ won't learn and they'll stop trying and caring about their jobs.

Roving Man: A large breeding farm needs a roving man. The roving man is actually the night foreman. He must have a comprehensive knowledge of horses, second only to the farm manager. His duties take him from one barn to another throughout the night, checking horses, assisting foaling mares, checking the yearlings in the pasture. The roving man checks on the employees in each barn, making sure they don't neglect any details. When an emergency arises in the middle of the night, the roving man will van a sick mare to the hospital or assume the duties of another employee so that person can go. In the case of an injured horse or a foaling mare, the roving man is in attendance. It is his call whether to notify the farm manager or veterinarian, so he must have the knowledge and experience to make the right decisions in a crisis.

Broodmare Manager: The broodmare manager is responsible for all mares that are pregnant, foaling and with foals at their sides. He must be knowledgeable about all aspects of teasing, breeding, foaling and young foals. He must have the technical knowledge to work closely with the veterinarian, plus have years of practical experience. The broodmare manager is usually the teasing man, which is a specialty in itself. He works closely with the night man or foaling man. He must have the knowledge to assist with a foaling that occurs during the daytime, when the foaling man is off duty.

The good broodmare manager genuinely likes mares. He understands them and knows how to read their body language. He has the necessary devotion to endure the long hours and sleepless nights of the breeding season.

Night Man/Foaling Man: The night man is also the foaling man. He works for the broodmare manager but is supervised by the roving man. This is a specialized position, requiring a great deal of veterinary knowledge and practical experience. The foaling man must be capable of assisting with a difficult foaling, knowing when to intervene and when to get help. He is a true equine midwife.

I like the night man to be a working position. He should walk down the aisles every hour, picking the piles of manure and setting them aside and filling the water buckets. The night man should check the horses' feed tubs for uneaten grain and adjust the foals' halters. He should look at the horses' feet and make note of any problems. In between rounds, he can clean halters and tack and brush the mares and foals. I don't care to pay someone just to sit on the couch in the watchroom. It's too easy for that person to fall asleep and miss a foaling. Keeping the night people busy saves labor for the daytime crew.

The rest of the year, the foaling man/night man is a night watchman, going through the barren/maiden mare barns, checking the stallions and going through the yearling barns. Any problems that arise during the night, such as cast horses or colics, are his responsibility.

A 20- or 24-stall barn of broodmares and foals is enough for a night man. If his charges are barren/maiden mares or yearlings, he is able to check about 40 to 60 stalls.

Barren/Maiden Mare Manager: The barren/maiden mare manager has many of the qualities of the broodmare man. He must have technical and practical knowledge about teasing and breeding mares equal to that of the broodmare manager. On a small farm, they might be the same man. This foreman is in charge of fillies that come off the racetrack. It is his responsibility to change them from racehorses to mothers in one year, a job that requires tact and intuition.

The foaling man, the broodmare manager and the barren/maiden mare manager all have a gift for understanding mares. They can read a mare's body language and tell you about her health, attitude and reproductive status before anybody else.

Yearling Manager: The yearling manager is responsible for young horses from the time they are weaned from their dams until they are sold. Since a breeding farm's financial well-being may depend on the profitable sales of its yearlings, it is vital that they be under the care and supervision of an expert.

The yearling manager must understand what it takes to develop a weanling into a healthy, substantial yearling that will impress buyers and bring a good price. He must know how to feed and exercise yearlings and be familiar with common injuries, leg problems, growth and metabolic disorders. It takes experience to look at a young horse and see if it is developing correctly or if special attention is needed from the veterinarian, farrier or nutritionist.

The yearling man knows showmanship and salesmanship and teaches it to his grooms. He knows that when a yearling is shown to a prospective buyer, that colt or filly must be groomed and trained to perfection. A skillful yearling man can present the young horse's good qualities while minimizing its faults and shortcomings.

One quality the yearling man must have is the right personality to work with young, impressionable horses. He supervises all lessons in leading, loading, bathing, standing for the farrier and for presentation. Patient but firm, he is not intimidated by bad behavior and he *always* controls his temper. This calm, confident personality produces sound, well-mannered young horses for the sales ring and racetrack.

Rotating Man: Earlier in this chapter, I discussed the importance of grooms. The best example of a good groom is the *rotating man*. A rotating man is a specialist groom who can manage his co-workers' horses when any particular groom has the day off. For every six grooms, you need one rotating man. A good rotating man works six days a week in a different barn every day, replacing whoever is off-duty and leaving the barns in better shape than he found them. He knows the temperament of each horse and all details of their feed and care. He understands the groom he's replacing, how he operates and he fills the void. He must be a good horseman and able to accomplish a lot in a day to do this.

Stallion Manager: The man who handles the stallions is a person of special talents and character. This horseman understands the personality of each and handles him accordingly. The stallion man is responsible for valuable animals in situations that are often dangerous. He must have the concentration, steady nerves and good reactions to handle stallions safely. The best stallion men have a personality that commands respect from the stallion without exciting or provoking him. A stallion manager may look after his horses for many years. He develops a relationship and an understanding with them that must be respected.

The grooms who work for the stallion manager are specialized grooms, trained to deal with difficult horses and to assist with the cover. The stallion manager has the responsibility to choose employees with these capabilities and to instruct them. He and his team are in charge of extremely expensive animals, perhaps worth millions of dollars. They must display the highest degree of professionalism.

Staffing Requirements: Every barn requires a foreman. Any barn housing more than eight or ten horses requires a groom to assist the foreman. A 20-stall broodmare barn needs two people on duty - one manager or foreman and one groom for every ten stalls. This assumes an average workload of 10 mares with foals turned out 12 hours a day. But everyone needs a day off, so a 20-stall barn will require a rotating man, bringing the total to three people. This gives the barn at least two people on duty regardless of days off.

Yearlings are labor-intensive horses and the workload increases as the sales draw near. Exercising and grooming the yearlings takes time - there are no shortcuts and you must staff for it. Yearling grooms are put in charge of five yearlings each. A 20-stall yearling barn needs four grooms and a rotating man.

In Conclusion: Consider the opportunity you have in training people who will take their place in the industry and in society. Here is the chance to teach what never appears in books about bloodlines and breeding theories, about great horses and great people and about the honesty and courage that made them great. Explain to your grooms what makes a particular broodmare so valuable and your hopes for her offspring. Instruct them to shake hands and greet people by name. Talk about business, about ethics, about courtesy and about commitment and talk about why you love horses. You are molding people as much as you are training employees. Instill your values as well as your methods. It can be one of the most rewarding aspects of the business.

FARM HIERARCHY

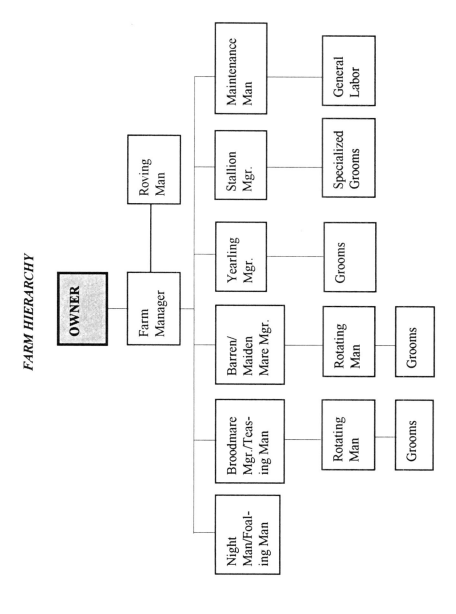

Chapter 15

General Farm Routine

The general farm routine is anything but routine. It's the difference, the edge, the deciding factor between a good farm that produces a few good horses, and the superior farm that produces many good horses and the occasional great one. This chapter covers a variety of subjects that can help you gain that edge.

Turnout: Elsewhere in this book I've talked about turning out your horses but the subject bears repeating. Turning out horses is a practice I believe in strongly. It's natural for a horse to be outside. Arrange your schedules so all horses are outside more than they're inside.

Many people allow the horses' turnout schedule to be disrupted for the convenience of the staff, the veterinarian or the farrier. This is a mistake. A common scenario is to keep the horse in his stall for a 9:00 a.m. appointment with the veterinarian, who may not arrive until 11:00 a.m. The horse is treated, then put back into his stall by his groom who delays the horse's turnout until after lunch. By now it is afternoon and half the day is gone. The horse has spent half the day confined to his stall simply for convenience. His routine has been disrupted. This can result in a sick foal, a cranky or a yearling that's climbing the walls because he's not out with his buddies. It upsets the mare you are trying to settle. This is poor management. Turn the horse out when he's supposed to go out. When the veterinarian or farrier arrives, bring the horse in from the paddock. Don't compromise the horse's well-being for convenience.

How to Turn Out Horses: Turning out horses sounds like the simplest job in the world. It is not. Turning out a horse involves several steps, each carrying the risk of injury to horse and handler. Accidents can be avoided only when the handler understands what can go wrong and takes steps to prevent it.

To understand what is risky about turning a horse out, look at it from the horse's point of view. The horse was fed in his stall and left to relax for a few hours. The barn is quiet, the scenery is the same. A person walks in the barn, which tells the horse something is going to change. The person enters the stall, puts on the halter and leads the horse out of the safety of his stall, away from the other horses in the barn. The horse is led outside to a world of open spaces and new sights, fresh air with new scents. The change is stimulating. There may be other horses outside that lift their heads and call and those inside may answer. The horses outside may start to run. All this is exciting to the horse. It is natural for him to respond by attempting to bolt or play up. He may even break free from his handler.

All this must be anticipated. Safety in turning out horses starts with knowing what excites the horse and minimizing his exposure to it. The horse must be handled so he feels both restrained and reassured. Control the environment so when a horse breaks loose - and this will happen - he cannot run into the road, into machinery or into other horses.

The first step is knowing where you are going with the horse. A large farm has many paddocks, laid out to fit the contours of the land. It can be difficult to describe verbally which paddock a particular horse should occupy. Paddocks must be clearly labeled and a map belongs inside the barn of all paddocks that serve it. The map must make it absolutely clear which is "paddock B-7," for instance. Never leave the barn with a horse without knowing where you are going.

The order of turn out is important. Horses that go to the most distant paddocks and pastures are turned out first so they are not excited by walking past other horses on the way. They are brought in last for the same reason. The first two horses to go outside should be taken out in pairs and the last two horses to come in the barn should come inside in pairs. Never take one horse outside alone or leave one horse alone in a pasture. Yearling colts are turned out by themselves in paddocks, but lead two colts from adjacent paddocks inside in pairs. Do not leave one colt in a paddock by himself when all the others have been brought inside.

This paddock is clearly marked.

(Photo courtesy of Suzie Oldham)

Make sure you have the horse's attention as you lead him into the paddock and particularly as you go through the gate. A distracted horse may jump and hit the gateposts. As you close the gate, bring his head around so he faces you, then lead him away from the gate a few feet. Keeping the horse's head facing you, release the lead shank quietly and step back two paces. You must be out of striking distance in the event that the horse jumps or kicks out.

Another hazard of turnout is the chance of putting horses into a paddock that already has horses in it. If the field is large or the light is low, it is easy to make this mistake. This is a particularly dangerous risk with stallions. Avoid this by having both a latch and a chain on each paddock gate. When the paddock is not occupied, the gate is closed with the latch only. When a horse is turned out in the paddock, the latch and the chain are fastened. Even in the dark, you are able to find the chain on the gate and know whether the paddock is occupied or not.

Feed Management and Feeding Routines: Store your grain and hay in such a way that the supply of feed is rotated. New bags of grain should go behind the last few bags of the previous batch. Hay storage must be arranged so each shipment is fed until gone. This requires some planning. You need to designate several areas in the hay storage building for various shipments. The oldest supplies must be fed first - do not pile new hay on top of older hay. Burying a load of good quality hay for half a year is commonly done, but it is poor management. Managed correctly, the hay you're feeding will never be more than a few months old.

Whoever is responsible for feeding pastured horses must know how many horses are in each pasture. Take a head count every time the field is entered. A missing horse could be colicking somewhere just out of sight. After the horses have been checked, look down the fence lines for broken rails.

When filling the hay racks, carry a bucket for the baling wires and twine. These items are dangerous and should never be left in a horse pasture. Always have one or two lead shanks with you, in case a horse has to be taken out of the pasture.

Bedding: I use wheat straw for bedding. It's bright, it's absorbent enough to soak up urine and it shakes out easily. Oat straw is too fine. It contains a lot of dust and chaff, which is unhealthy. Rye straw is bright and it lasts a long time, but it's not as absorbent and it takes too long to shake out. Rye straw takes three times as long to shake out and bed a stall as does wheat straw. Your labor costs will reflect this.

We have used wood shavings for horses that tend to eat their straw bedding. It does absorb the urine and they won't eat it. I don't care for it because it really sticks in the manes and tails. It takes the grooms a long time to comb the shavings out every day.

Bed your stalls thickly, about eight inches deep and pack it tightly. The horse must be able to lie down and get up without ever contacting the bare floor. In summer, it's important to keep it dry. The drier the bedding, the better for the haircoat. In the winter, bed even more deeply for warmth.

Rubber mats are becoming very popular and with good reason. While the stall still needs the same amount of bedding, rubber mats fit well over asphalt floors. They are beneficial for horses that have to stand in the stall a lot, such as sales yearlings or stallions. Some horses paw and wear their hooves down badly. Rubber mats help maintain a good hoof condition on a horse that paws and they eliminate slipping.

Proper Stall Cleaning: The best way to clean a stall is from the inside to the outside: Remove the piles of manure and put the old, dry bedding around the sides. Clean the center of the stall down to the asphalt, removing all the wet, soiled straw. Cover the center with the old bedding from the sides. When the sides of the stall are exposed, clean that area by removing any wet spots and raking and sweeping up the chaff. When the entire floor of the stall is clean, spread a new bale of straw over the old bedding, patting it down firmly and banking the sides again. A firm cushion of bedding keeps the horse dry and prevents him from scraping his hocks on the asphalt. This must be done every day. In an exceptional case, such as a broodmare and foal which cannot be turned out because of illness or injury, it may need to be done twice a day.

The secret of maintaining clean stalls is keeping them picked out. No one, whether he is the owner, the farm manager or a groom should walk past a pile of manure. Slide your hands under the straw beneath the pile, as if you were picking up a bird's nest, and put it under the waterer where it won't be trampled into the clean bedding. This is parasite control, showmanship and good management.

Muck Sacks: I use muck sacks in place of the big muck baskets. A muck sack is a burlap bag six or eight feet square. It holds about three bushels of manure. It's easy to fill and dump into a wagon or spreader and easy to store. Muck baskets are bulky and harder to store and one more thing for horses and employees to trip over.

Rodent Control: We use the most efficient, effective and environmentally sound method available for controlling rodents. We keep cats. Cats are quiet and unobtrusive around horses, unlike dogs that are bred for ratting and mousing. Well-fed cats will mouse for fun and sport and, so far, they have no union. Female employees will often volunteer to feed and care for the cats.

Record-Keeping: Keep a record card on each stall door. It should include the name of the sire and dam of the occupant, the owner, amount and times of feed. It should include a place for special instructions, such as daily care relating to an injury. These records must be kept up-to-date because the grooms and night people depend on them for directions.

Radios: Earlier, I said that radios are not necessary in the warm room or anyplace in the barn. While this is true, a radio can be useful for giving information on severe weather. And grooms, especially young people, enjoy having music to work by. Chances are, this music will be loud and raucous. If you allow a radio in the barn, you must control it. Radios must not be played loudly while the horses are in the barn and should be turned off when you have visitors. An on-off switch next to the bank of light switches near the entrance of the barn lets you control the radio.

Worming and Vaccinations: Regular worming and vaccinations are essential to produce and maintain healthy horses. Disease and parasite infestation not only rob horses of their potential but can be life-threatening. Racing is the ultimate test of a horse and nothing less than optimum health can meet this challenge.

I am giving you the schedule that we use for worming and vaccinating our horses. However, I urge you to consult your veterinarian to develop your own program. Horses in your locale may have slightly different requirements.

Worming is done 10 times a year. We tube worm twice a year, roughly six months apart. We use paste-type wormers eight times a year. Ten days after each tube worming, we take fecal samples and check for the presence of parasites. Any horse showing signs of a problem with parasite infestation is treated again, with a follow-up fecal sample.

Parasites can develop resistance to specific wormers if the same type of wormer is used over and over. Use a variety of wormers and rotate them to prevent this. We use three different types, or families, of wormers. They are: (1) ivermectin, products such as Zimectrin, Eqvalan; (2) pyrantel pamoate, products such as Strongid paste, Strongid C; (3) benzimidazoles, products such as Panacur, Rintal, Telmin, Anthelcide EQ, Cutter, and Benzelmin. I will refer to them as Product #1, #2, or #3.

In January, we begin with a paste wormer, such as product #2. Six weeks later we use another type of paste wormer, either product #1 or # 3. We worm again in six weeks, rotating each time between the types of product. In mid spring, we tube worm with a double dose of Product #2 and run fecal samples 10 days later to check on the results of the program. We continue to rotate wormers at the six-week intervals until fall when we tube worm again with the same double dose of #2. Fecal samples are taken again and tested. Then we pick up again with the rotation of paste wormers through the winter.

The summer wormings may need to be done more often, with slightly longer intervals in the middle of winter. Your veterinarian can advise you of the proper intervals between wormings for your area. It is important that fecal sample testing follow the twice-annual tube wormings. Rotate the families of wormers.

There is a new worming product available that is made to be fed daily, eliminating the need for some of these wormings. It is from the Product #2 class and is quite effective when fed exactly according to directions. With young horses that are kept outside as our horses are, it is difficult to administer in the prescribed manner. When horses eat outside in a group, you are not able to determine that each horse has consumed his share of the feed with the wormer in it. For this reason, we do not use this product. But for horses that are fed inside their stalls twice daily, it is a good alternative.

Vaccinations: I will identify the types of vaccinations according to disease rather than brand names. Brand names are not important. What is important is to use a vaccine that your veterinarian has experience in using and has confidence in. Perhaps most important are the schedules for vaccinations. To maintain a high level of protection, each horse needs the right shots at the right times. Horses that ship in to us must come with vaccination records, which are checked as they step off the van. Any lapses in vaccinations are corrected immediately. Any horse without vaccination records is assumed to be unvaccinated.

These schedules are appropriate for horses in Kentucky. Breeders in other locations may need to consider Potomac Horse Fever vaccinations and Strangles vaccinations, although these are not generally given in Kentucky. It is important to consult your veterinarian to determine which vaccinations are needed in your area. *Tetanus:* Tetanus vaccinations are given at 30, 60 and 90 days to foals. Pregnant mares are vaccinated 30 days prior to foaling. Barren mares, other adult horses and yearlings receive an annual booster. A horse with no history of vaccinations needs the series described for foals.

Encephalitis or Sleeping Sickness: Sleeping sickness vaccinations are given exactly as the tetanus. Many times these vaccinations are combined into one shot by the manufacturer. In our part of the country, sleeping sickness vaccines are limited to the Eastern-Western strain of encephalitis. A farm in the extreme southern United States may be in an area where it is advisable to vaccinate for the Venezuelan variety as well. Your veterinarian will know if you are located in such an area.

Influenza: Foals are vaccinated for influenza at 30, 60 and 90 days. Pregnant mares are vaccinated 30 days before foaling, while barren mares and other adult horses receive an annual booster. Yearlings are vaccinated every 60 days for influenza.

Rhinopneumonitis: Foals are vaccinated at 30, 60 and 90 days. Every other horse on the farm is vaccinated for Rhino at 60 day intervals. Rhinopneumonitis is a common cause of abortion in broodmares, wiping out entire crops in past years. Don't take any chances with this disease. Every horse must be vaccinated every 60 days against Rhino.

Botulism: Botulism is a problem in our area of the country, so we vaccinate against it. All horses require an initial series of three shots against botulism. After this series of three shots, all horses get an annual booster. Foals are vaccinated at 120, 150 and 180 days. Horses that have never received the vaccine must have the initial three-shot series at 30-day intervals. Foaling mares that ship in with no vaccination records are vaccinated in the eighth and ninth months of gestation and again 30 days prior to foaling. If we know that the foaling mare has had the three-shot series, we give her only the booster shot 30 days before her due date.

Rabies: Rabies is not common in horses, but it is deadly and preventable. We vaccinate foals at 120 days and pregnant mares in January or 30 days before foaling. All other horses are vaccinated against rabies annually.

EVA: Equine viral arteritis is an infectious disease caused by a virus and characterized by an upper respiratory infection and, occasionally, by abortion in broodmares. It is not usually fatal and is endemic only in certain areas. Most Thoroughbreds foals and yearlings are not vaccinated against EVA for two reasons:

(1) In well-managed Thoroughbred populations, the disease has not been a serious enough problem to warrant vaccination. The Thoroughbred industry relies on good management practices, such as isolation of new horses, to control EVA. We have not had any problem with this disease that would justify vaccination.

(2) There is a vaccine available to prevent EVA, but the use of the vaccine leaves a positive titer, or the measurable presence of antibodies, in the blood. A positive titer is also found in infected horses and there is no way to distinguish a vaccinated horse from an

infected one. Since many Thoroughbreds are shipped to Europe where a positive EVA titer will bar them from importation, we don't vaccinate for this disease. Some farms may have broodmares that have been vaccinated and stallions standing in Kentucky must have the vaccination by law. But no one vaccinates yearlings for EVA. If a young horse is a potential European export, it's important that he not carry the positive titer to EVA that a vaccination gives.

The Standardbred industry has had more experience with EVA and has taken deliberate steps to combat it by vaccination. Consequently, nearly all Standardbred horses will show a positive titer from the vaccine or from a natural immunity acquired due to exposure. If a test were developed that could tell the vaccinated horse from the infected horse, I suspect the Thoroughbred industry would follow suit.

Chapter 16

Thoughts on Life As a Horseman

Throughout this book I have explained what you need to know to be successful in the horse business. I have described how to make hard business decisions, how to see through the tricks and traps and how to determine the true value of horses apart from their reputations and beauty. These are the things I have learned in more than 50 years in the horse business. These are the methods that have helped me make a life in this industry and I hope they serve you well. But those 50 years have taught me more than just the horse business. Success is more than making money.

Life around horses is its own reward. Look past the dollar signs on each horse and enjoy the animals for their beauty. Remember the Bedouin saying that your pregnant mare has "treasure in her belly" and enjoy her pregnancy and foaling for the miracle that it is. Enjoy the foal racing in the pasture for its own sake. Feed your racehorses carrots and kiss them on the nose. Keep a pensioner if it pleases you. *Enjoy your horses* .

The horse is the most noble and generous of God's creations. A good racehorse will give his life trying to finish a race simply because he was asked to do so. Allow yourself to be moved and humbled by this spirit. Treat all your horses with the respect and kindness due such a gallant animal. *Be good to the creatures entrusted to you.*

One of my reasons for writing this book is to help bring new people into the business. If I have helped you to become successful, then share your knowledge with others. Bring another new person into the business and let him benefit from your experience. Give a deserving young person a break. You have had some good luck - create some good luck for someone else. What goes around comes around and your good turn will come back to you, if only in peace of mind. *Be generous with your knowledge and support.*

Remember your family and your values. All the racing success in the world can't begin to replace the small accomplishments of sons and daughters, grandsons and granddaughters. Make time for them. Make time for going to church, for doing charity or volunteer work or whatever is in your power to make this a better world. Be thankful for what God had given you and be at peace with what He has not. If you are kind to your horses and your family and grateful to God, you are a success already. *Make time for God and family.*

The best of racing luck to you!

Joseph Lannon Taylor

INDEX

Other Fine Books for Your Racing Library

Specifications for Speed in the Racehorse: The Airflow Factors by Dr. W. Robert Cook. Dr. Cook explains why the way a horse breathes determines how far and how fast it can run. He tells you how the "airflow factors" can be seen and measured on the outside of the horse and gives you the same grading system he uses to evaluate yearlings for some of the world's most successful racehorse owners. This is the book that is changing the standards by which racehorses are being bred, bought and sold. Softcover 256 pages - $25.00.

Specifications for Speed: The Video based on the best-selling book by Dr. W. Robert Cook of Tufts University, this new video will show you how to determine the soundness of wind in any horse you own or plan to purchase. In this new video you will see how breathing affects the stride of the horse; how to measure jaw width for maximum airflow capacity; how RLN affects the airway of a horse; new electronic technology that evaluates airflow soundness and much more. $49.95

Training Thoroughbred Horses by Preston Burch. The training secrets of Hall of Fame trainer Preston Burch are once again available in his classic book. He explains how to select, train and campaign horses of all aptitudes to become tough, competitive winners. No Thoroughbred owner or trainer should be without this valuable book. Hardcover 128 pages - $19.95.

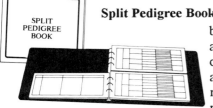

Split Pedigree Book. This book of pedigree forms is indispensable to the breeder. It contains separate pedigree pages for sires and dams. Fill in the bottom pages with the pedigrees of your mares and the top pages with the pedigrees of all stallions you are considering. The pedigree of each resulting foal is laid out before you. Looseleaf 40 pages $19.00.

The Science of Bloodstock Breeding by B. Vijay. In simple, easy-to-

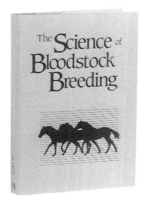

understand language, the author explains how to breed a fast horse. He gives you the five-step process of rating stallions; tells you how to spot the four different types of "nicks"; details the theories of inbreeding and out-crossing; and, you'll learn why the new theory of the "International Outbred" seems to work. The book is filled with information you need to select good broodmares. You will learn the concept of dosage and how to use it to your advantage. **The Science of Bloodstock Breeding** should be on the bookshelf of everyone who breeds Thoroughbreds. Hardcover 422 pages -$39.00.

The Complete Guide to Claiming Thoroughbreds - Finding, Fixing, and Making Winners by Tom Ivers. Ivers tells you how to spot claimers at all price

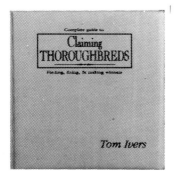

tags that you can improve and how to take two seconds off their time. He tells you why your horses will perform better with his simple, inexpensive method of feeding; you'll learn how to shoe to add speed; and why most claiming horses thrive by being raced frequently. He explains how to keep your horses sound with conditioning and exercise techniques, how to deal with lameness in any horse you acquire; why corticosteroids and similar drugs compound lameness problems. If you are serious about making a profit with claiming horses, this is the book for you. Looseleaf - 271 pages $69.00.

To order call us at (800) 635-6499 in the USA and Canada, (414) 725-0955 Worldwide (414) 725-0709 FAX.

Call for your *free* copy of our complete catalog of Hard-To-Find Books and Videos on Breeding and Racing. (800) 635-6499.

The Russell Meerdink Company, Ltd.
1555 South Park Avenue
Neenah, WI 54956

(800) 635-6499 in the USA and Canada (414) 725-0955 Worldwide

(414) 725-0709 FAX